METHOD IN THE PHYSICAL SCIENCES

International Library of Philosophy and Scientific Method

EDITOR: A. J. AYER
ASSISTANT EDITOR: BERNARD WILLIAMS

INDUCTIVE PROBABILITY by John Patrick Day.

SENSATION AND PERCEPTION: A History of the Philosophy of Perception by D. W. Hamlyn.

TRACTATUS LOGICO-PHILOSOPHICUS: Ludwig Wittgenstein's *Logisch-philosophische Abhandlung* with a new Translation by D. F. Pears and B. F. McGuinness and with the Introduction by Bertrand Russell.

PERCEPTION AND THE PHYSICAL WORLD by D. M. Armstrong.

HUME'S PHILOSOPHY OF BELIEF: A Study of His First *Inquiry* by Antony Flew.

KANT'S THEORY OF KNOWLEDGE: An Outline of One Central Argument in the *Critique of Pure Reason* by Graham Bird.

CONDITIONS FOR DESCRIPTION by Peter Zinkernagel, translated from the Danish by Olaf Lindum.

AN EXAMINATION OF PLATO'S DOCTRINES by I. M. Crombie.
I: Plato on Man and Society.   II: Plato on Knowledge and Reality.

PHENOMENOLOGY OF PERCEPTION by M. Merleau-Ponty, translated from the French by Colin Smith.

THE IDEA OF JUSTICE AND THE PROBLEM OF ARGUMENT by Chaim Perelman, translated from the French by John Petrie.

LECTURES ON PSYCHICAL RESEARCH by C. D. Broad. Incorporating the Perrott Lectures given in Cambridge University in 1959 and 1960.

THE VARIETIES OF GOODNESS by Georg Henrik von Wright.

METHOD IN THE PHYSICAL SCIENCES by G. Schlesinger.

SCIENCE, PERCEPTION AND REALITY by Wilfrid Sellars.

METHOD IN THE PHYSICAL SCIENCES

by

G. Schlesinger

Senior Lecturer in Philosophy, Australian National University

LONDON

ROUTLEDGE & KEGAN PAUL

NEW YORK : THE HUMANITIES PRESS

First published 1963
by Routledge & Kegan Paul Ltd.
Broadway House, 68–74 Carter Lane
London, E.C.4

Printed in Great Britain
by Richard Clay and Company, Ltd.
Bungay, Suffolk

CONTENTS

ACKNOWLEDGEMENTS   *page* vi

INTRODUCTION
  (1) Primary and Supplementary Principles   1
  (2) The Logical Basis of Methodological Principles   4

1   THE PRINCIPLE OF SIMPLICITY
  (1) Introduction   8
  (2) The Thesis of Nature's Simplicity   10
  (3) Simplicity and Verification   19
  (4) Simplicity and Falsifiability   26
  (5) The Principle of Simplicity in the History of Science 32
  (6) Dynamic Simplicity   36
  (7) Open and Closed Hypotheses   39
  (8) Conclusion   43

2   THE PRINCIPLE OF MICRO-REDUCTION
  (1) Introduction   45
  (2) Micro-reduction and Determinism   47
  (3) Physical and Logical Analysis   53
  (4) Macro-reduction in the History of Science   56
  (5) E. Mach and Atomism   61
  (6) The General Search for Atomic Theories   68
  (7) Conclusion   71

3   THE PRINCIPLE OF CONNECTIVITY
  (1) Introduction   73
  (2) Causality and Connectivity   74
  (3) E. Mach's Principle of Symmetry   79
  (4) The Resolvability of Particular Dispositions   84
  (5) N. R. Campbell's Principle of Symmetrical Uniform
      Association   89
  (6) P. W. Bridgman's Principle of Essential Connectivity   92
  (7) J. C. Maxwell's Criterion for Distinguishing between
      Real and Empty Predicates   95

CONTENTS

(8) The Uncertain Meaning of Maxwell's Criterion 100
(9) Conclusion 103

4 THE PRINCIPLE OF VERIFICATION
(1) Introduction 106
(2) The Technical–Physical–Logical Trichotomy 109
(3) Weak Verification 115
(4) The Comparative Function of Analysis: The Differential Aspect 122
(5) The General Function of Comparative Analysis 130
(6) Conclusion 134

INDEX 139

ACKNOWLEDGEMENTS

I should like to record my indebtedness to at least some of the people who have made my task possible. I am grateful to Mr. Gerd Buchdahl, Miss Diana Dyason and Professor Kurt Baier for the continual encouragement and advice they have given me. The latter has also read a part of the typescript and has offered valuable criticism, as have Professor John Passmore and Dr. Robert Brown. It is with pleasure and gratitude that I recall the lengthy and stimulating discussions I have had with Messrs. Brian Ellis and Bruce Benjamin on scientific methodology. To Mrs. N. J. Pearson and my wife Shulamith go my thanks for careful proof reading.

Nearly a quarter of the material of this book has appeared in print before, between the years 1959–1961. Acknowledgements are due to the editors of the *British Journal of the Philosophy of Science*, *Philosophical Review* and *Philosophy of Science* for giving me permission to use this material in the present work.

G. S.

INTRODUCTION

I. PRIMARY AND SUPPLEMENTARY PRINCIPLES

THE amount of philosophical writing available on any of the principles studied in this essay is small compared to the vast literature that exists on such subjects as the principle of the uniformity of nature or the principle of causality. Even less has been said about the nature, status and origin of the *type* of principle that forms the subject of our inquiry. This ought not to seem surprising once we realize that our principles are supplementary to those universal methodological principles—often referred to also as *a priori* postulates or metaphysical doctrines presupposed by science—which have attracted so much philosophical interest and discussion. Our principles which are principles *within* science are secondary in relation to the more fundamental principles which *precede* science and which guarantee the possibility of discourse in general.

This, however, does not detract from the significance of the results obtainable through inquiring into the nature of supplementary principles. For these principles will not be studied merely for their own sake but for the sake of the light they shed on the entire conceptual groundwork of the scientific enterprise. By treating them as vital forces animating the growth mechanism of systemized knowledge one gains deeper insight into the dynamic structure of science by a better understanding of the nature of these forces.

A few words of explanation are called for as to what these two types of principles are and how they are related to one another. Firstly, supplementary principles always presuppose some primary principle. The former are superimposed upon the latter and amplify them. Secondly, supplementary principles are not indispensable for making inferences possible from matters of fact in the way the more

I

fundamental principles are. If the contrary of a supplementary principle were true we could still make sense of the phenomena around us and be able to discourse about them, whereas in the case of the more primary principles this does not seem to be possible.

Let me explain the first point first. An example of a supplementary principle would be the doctrine—held in the 19th century, by some explicitly and by others implicitly—that all the laws of physics are reducible to Newtonian mechanics. This is a supplementary principle presupposing and restricting the scope of a more-general principle, which asserts that we are not living in a chaotic universe, but that phenomena are governed by universal regularities and that it is within the power of human beings to discover these regularities and formulate them into theories and laws. The primary principle states in general that phenomena are governed by some laws, whereas the supplementary principle specifies the type of laws there are; it delineates the area to be searched in our pursuit of those laws.

By the same token, the principle asserting that all the laws of nature are reducible to sub-atomic physics, as maintained by some spokesmen of the movement for the Unity of Science,[1] or that the true laws of nature when expressed in words never contain the terms 'some' or 'except'[2] are supplementary principles. So is the better known and more generally accepted principle prescribing that, in cases where two laws account equally well for the same range of phenomena, the one represented by a mathematically simpler function should always be chosen. The general principle about the existence of laws does not specify how to distinguish between rival candidates that may present themselves, whereas this last principle—an important variation of the principle of simplicity —does give us this additional information.

Or, for example, Keynes' famous postulate of limited variety, is a primary principle. It is a postulate to ensure the existence of 'natural kinds'. In the absence of natural kinds every entity would have a law for itself and generalization would be impossible. But a principle informing us how to recognize natural kinds, which are the significant features of entities and properties determining whether they belong to the same natural kind or not, is a secondary principle.[3]

Or again the principle of connectivity according to which two

[1] See Chapter 2.   [2] See Chapter 1.   [3] See Chapter 4.

2

physical systems never differ in one and only one disposition—is a secondary principle. It is, in fact, an extension of the principle of causality. For every physical property or disposition is an instantiation of the principle 'same event same cause'. For if this principle were continually violated, no statements could be made about properties or dispositions. A body could not be said, for instance, to be of a given mass, for to be of a given mass means that *whenever* placed in the neighborhood of another body an acceleration of a certain magnitude will be induced. Thus, that a material body may have the disposition always to induce the same acceleration under the same circumstances is an exemplification of the principle 'same cause same effect'. So is the fact that a body may possess hardness, elasticity, density or colour. Therefore, a principle which presupposes the existence of dispositions and prescribes the way in which they may occur, that for instance they may never occur in isolation, is a supplementary or amplifying principle.

Now to the second feature whereby the two types of principles may be distinguished from one another. We call primary those principles which are required in general to guarantee the possibility of human discourse. If a primary principle were constantly violated it seems evident that the universe would so markedly differ from what it is now that language would altogether be inconceivable. Supplementary principles, on the other hand, are of no such fundamental nature. One cannot envisage any catastrophic consequences for intelligibility and communication in general, if the contrary of a supplementary principle were true.

Take, for example, the contrary of the principle of causality which is 'every event is uncaused' or 'no two events have the same cause'. If this were true we could not talk of dispositions as pointed out before. But neither could we have the concept of a physical body. We are cognizant of physical bodies through the dispositions they possess. Thus, in fact, our language could have no nouns, adjectives or verbs. The same situation would arise if the principle asserting that there are natural kinds were never instantiated.

Because of the fundamental role primary principles play in all discourse they are of equal interest to all departments of philosophy. The existence of our principles, on the other hand, only makes itself felt in the course of a closer examination of the methods employed by practical scientists. The character and scope of our principles cannot adequately be discussed without reference to actual scientific procedures and results. They form part of the subject matter proper of the specific discipline of the philosophy of science.

2. THE LOGICAL BASIS OF METHODOLOGICAL PRINCIPLES

My aim is to study the nature of principles actually operative in science. I intend to deal with principles which have been employed and have produced results prior to any attempts to formulate them explicitly; principles which were implicit in the workings of scientists without their necessarily being aware of them; principles which motivated the choice of strategies and shaped the path along which the explorers of nature proceeded. There is a wide gap separating ideal principles set up in the abstract—no matter how sound and attractive theoretically they may seem, and those actually operative in science. One falls easily into error through ignoring this gap.

It is, however, by no means simple to keep to the task of giving an authentic description and detached analysis of the procedures of scientists rather than to embark upon a rational reconstruction of those procedures. One is, after all, at least as much interested in the question of the logical foundations or the rationale of methodological rules as in their contents. The knowledge of the latter without the knowledge of the former does not provide much insight into the conceptual structure of science. There is little philosophical interest in rules of thumb or in inexplicable methodological principles. Consequently, the student of methodology is apt to start by setting up first what is to him a satisfactory logical basis and then go on to find principles which can be made to rest on such basis. I hope that in the course of our subsequent discussion of the individual principles it will become evident how the problem of justification has been the main source of trouble in methodology, and how many of the difficulties the student of methodology is bound to encounter in the course of his studies arise directly or indirectly out of this problem.

As the justification of methodological principles is the most central issue in this subject, it is important to ask how a justification might be attempted. In general one can envisage three possible ways. First of all there is empirical justification, which consists in a demonstration that a given methodological rule is rooted in the very nature of the universe. Empirical justification involves an attempt to show that a certain established feature of the physical world demands or permits a given form of procedure. The principle of simplicity has, for instance, often been regarded as justifiable on such grounds. It was believed that nature itself is in certain respects simple, and therefore if under specified circumstances we follow the rule to choose the simplest of the available hypotheses, we are bound to give a more truthful description of the laws that actually govern nature. In the next chapter we shall consider in some detail the idea that on an inductive basis, from the past results of science, one might establish the simplicity of nature and thus justify empirically the principle of simplicity.

Another way to defend a principle is to show that it is logically entailed by some other principle of already established and acknowledged status. An example of this could be given if we assumed, with a considerable number of philosophers, that all theory construction was guided by the principle of falsifiability. In other words, suppose we assume that scientific method proper is a continual striving to produce theories and laws as highly vulnerable to experimental refutation as possible. Then if indeed it could be shown, as has been claimed by K. R. Popper, that what is intuitively the simplest of alternative hypotheses is also always the most falsifiable one,[1] the principle of simplicity would be justified in this second way. Or again, since we assume the validity of the principle of causality and also accept the theory of evolution according to which complex systems evolved from more simple ones, then if these two assumptions together indeed entailed that the properties of complex systems must be explicable in terms of the properties of their constituent elements—as claimed by Oppenheim and Putnam[2]—then their principle of micro-reduction would also be justified in this way.

A third way of justifying a principle would be to show that it is analytically true; that anything not done in accordance with it would by definition not be science; that the procedure prescribed by it is what scientists do by virtue of the fact that they are scientists. Some of the 'weak' versions of the verifiability principle may be regarded as an illustration. It is often said that the verifiability principle states, that any proposition that cannot be verified—and by verification we mean that is has *some* relevance to observable facts—

---

[1] Cf. Chapter 1.   [2] Cf. Chapter 2.

is meaningless. 'Meaningless' may here be read, 'is not to be included within science', since whether an unverifiable proposition has any other meaning is not a question that concerns science. But, by definition, scientific method is that approach which investigates nature in order to account for its phenomena. Propositions without empirical import cannot be said to account for phenomena and are therefore to be excluded from science. Anything justified in this third way would no longer be regarded as a methodological principle within science, but as a part of the definition of science itself.

The principles to be considered in this essay seem, however, to defy all attempts to place them on any of the afore-mentioned logical bases. In the course of an extended study of the nature of these principles one becomes more and more convinced that the pattern of scientists' activities is moulded not only by what is logically or empirically required for the attainment of the declared objectives of science. For some of the constraints shaping the path followed by the pursuers of scientific knowledge are self-imposed; certain lines of action are adopted, others rejected, not by reason but by preference. Some of the factors that determine the conduct of scientists are provided from within, generated by the predispositions and predilections of the human mind.

This does not mean that the ultimate origins of the principles to be dealt with here lie completely in irreducible primitive urges not relateable to any features of external reality. Only, that they cannot be shown—in as simple and straightforward a fashion as one would wish—to be directly imposed by the nature of the physical world, neither can they be exhibited as immediate logical entailments of some universally accepted principles nor as forming an obvious part of the definition of science itself.

But the impossibility of synoptic description is a sign of the wealth of our subject. Because of the delicate balancing of the principles of methodology between indeterminacy and tentativeness on the one hand and concreteness and productivity on the other; between metaphysical rules or the conventional rules of language and the laws and theories of the empirical sciences, the intricate origins of the scientists' methodological apparatus cannot be exposed to view except through an extensive study. The present essay aims at initiating such a study in the course of which the manner in which the different principles derive to varying extents from deep-seated predilections, conceptual necessities and objective realities may gradually emerge.

The four principles we are going to discuss are important representatives of their kind. There is no reason to think that many more of their type may not be found in science. Indeed, just as it is the unending task of the scientist to observe the immense variety presented by nature to our senses, to endeavour to penetrate it and to identify the underlying discernible common features and express them in terms of principles, theories and laws of science, so it is the unending task of the student of the methods of science to observe the diversity of tactics and devices employed by scientists in the course of their endeavours to elicit from nature these principles, theories and laws and to try to recognize common features underlying these variform manoeuvrings and to formulate them in turn into the principles, theories and laws of methodology.

I

THE PRINCIPLE
OF SIMPLICITY

I. INTRODUCTION

THE important role played by the principle of simplicity as an adjudicator between rival scientific theories has been widely acknowledged. The principle of simplicity may be said to enjoy the most universal approval of all the principles to be dealt with in this book. There seems to be complete agreement between philosophers that it is one of the basic rules of scientific methodology not to multiply unnecessarily the entities admitted into one's theories, and to choose always the simplest of alternative hypotheses.

But universal agreement goes no farther than this. There is a great diversity of opinion about the correct interpretation, justification and application of this rule.

Firstly: Is the principle an expression of the underlying simple structure of nature itself? That is, does nature itself always prefer the simplest way to produce a certain result and is it in consequence of this that we should choose the simplest of alternative hypotheses which may entail the same phenomenon?

For a long time this explanation was taken for granted as the correct one. 'Nature does not by many things which can be done by a few', said Galileo; 'Nature does nothing in vain', said Newton. It is also well known that the firm belief in the ultimate simplicity of nature has inspired scientists like Galileo, Kepler, Newton, Maupertuis or even Einstein in some of their greatest accomplishments.

8

Lately, however, this view has been seriously questioned, and nowadays few philosophers would openly subscribe to it. There is, nevertheless, a need to discuss it in detail for two reasons. The first and main reason is that the thesis that nature is basically simple and that the principle is a direct expression of this simplicity holds out too great a fascination to many minds for it to be willingly abandoned completely. Secondly, those who oppose this thesis do not make quite clear the real reasons that make the thesis untenable. It is necessary, therefore, to clarify what precisely is involved in a statement about the simplicity of nature and why it cannot be held.

If we agree to renounce the claim that nature is intrinsically simple, we encounter a second problem: What gives authority to this principle? The view that the principle rests on no deeper foundations than that it is simpler to adopt a simple hypothesis than a more complex one, and that we are therefore advised to adopt the principle on grounds of convenience, is not a very popular one. Thus there have been various attempts to invest this methodological rule with a more dignified status than that of a mere rule of convenience. In the course of our discussion we shall consider some of the theses put forward claiming to exhibit the principle of simplicity as a direct outcome of certain fundamental features of the scientific theories.

The third problem is in a way even more fundamental than the first two: What precisely does the term 'simple' mean; what is the definition of simplicity? Can one identify in every case the simplest of rival hypotheses and if so, how? In a way this problem comes before the others, as one cannot adequately discuss the character of the principle of simplicity before one has got a clear notion of the term 'simplicity' contained in it. On the other hand, as there are various concepts of simplicity, it is only after one has agreed on the logical basis and function of the principle that one knows which concept of simplicity is the relevant one. Thus these problems are interdependent and have to be treated jointly. As to the solution of this last problem, here again we encounter a wide variety of opinions ranging from the plain assertion that simplicity is an unanalysable notion, which can only be sensed intuitively, to the various suggestions for the development of elaborate and rigorous mathematical criteria for simplicity.

I have formulated three problems right at the outset to give some indication—to use a paradoxical phrase—of the complex nature of simplicity. To gain a deeper insight into the nature of our problem we shall now inspect more closely some particular views on each of these questions.

2. THE THESIS OF NATURE'S SIMPLICITY

The idea that nature is governed by simple laws is a most captivating one. Assuming that there are no objective grounds for this idea, one could make a number of suggestions about the subjective origin of this idea. Everything is simple when understood, and as our knowledge advances matters do look less complicated than they looked before. The subjective pleasant feeling that develops with our difficulties of comprehension being gradually overcome; the sense of relief that arises when at last we grasp the relevant features of a problem and become the masters of the situation may have led to the belief that nature is simple.

Another source to point to as the possible subjective origin of the doctrine of nature's simplicity, would be the reassuring character of such a doctrine. If nature's laws are simple we may hope that eventually we shall unravel all the mysteries of the universe. Thus the doctrine offers great encouragement to its adherents.

But of course, such suggestions can in no way serve as a positive argument against those who support their belief in the simplicity of nature by objective evidence. The only adequate way to criticize them is to examine their arguments.

Nor is there any good reason to say that the simplicity of nature could in principle never inductively be established. The notion that there might be genuine grounds on which one could reject *ab initio* any attempts to show empirically that nature is simple derives, I believe, from a remark made by B. Russell in his paper 'On The Notion of Cause':

> Moreover it would be fallacious to argue inductively from the state of the advanced sciences to the future state of the others, for it may well be that the advanced sciences advanced simply because hitherto their subject matter has obeyed simple and easily ascertainable laws, while the subject matter of other sciences has not done so.[1]

Whether or not this was intended by Russell, his argument might easily be interpreted as saying: there is a fundamental difference

---

[1] B. Russell, *Mysticism and Logic* (Pelican Books, 1953), p. 193.

between the way the fact that all the observed ravens in the past were black supports the generalization that all the ravens in the universe are black, and the way the fact that all the hitherto discovered laws of nature were simple might serve as a basis for the generalization that all the laws of nature are simple. In the former case no convincing reason could be suggested why, if a considerable proportion of ravens were in fact not black, all the ravens we came across were black. In the latter case, however, it may very well be contended that in fact the overwhelming majority of nature's laws are extremely complex, so much so, that our minds could never comprehend them. It is possible that only a very minute part of nature's laws are simple enough to be discoverable and understandable but obviously all the laws we do succeed in discovering belong to this small and unrepresentative group of laws.

However, this argument is correct only if we assign a particular meaning to the term 'simple'. If the supporters of the doctrine of nature's simplicity interpret the term 'simple' to mean 'not too complex to be discovered by human beings' then, indeed, even in principle the doctrine could never be established inductively. It would obviously be a fallacy to conclude that nature's laws are simple, when by definition we cannot discover anything but simple laws.

But the term 'simple' may be defined in other ways. Suppose we define a simple law as a relationship between physical parameters that can be represented by an equation of the form $y = f(x_1, x_2, \ldots x_n)$. As long as there exist functions more complex than f, but still humanly comprehensible, the doctrine could in principle be established. For if we could show that none of the relevant[1] relationships hitherto discovered in nature had to be represented by functions more complicated than f, then this would count as inductive evidence that nature is governed by simple laws. The proposition asserting nature's simplicity would be a status not inferior to any other proposition held on inductive grounds.

I do not think, therefore, that there is any positive evidence against the possibility of empirically establishing the doctrine of the simplicity of the universe. The real reason why the doctrine cannot be held is that there is no positive evidence to support it.

[1] For, as we shall see later, it is impossible for all the relationships in nature to be simple. We must therefore assume also that we succeeded in describing clearly the type of relationships to which the principle applies.

Furthermore, nobody has so far succeeded in even formulating the doctrine in such a manner that any evidence could be relevant to it.

I shall now examine in detail a recent attempt to establish the thesis of nature's simplicity by empirical evidence. I shall refer to Professor R. O. Kapp's paper 'Ockham's Razor and the Unification of Physical Science'.[1] Kapp's paper has the great merit of being provocatively bold and outspoken. Whereas many people who hold beliefs similar to his do not articulate them, he does not hesitate to state his position clearly and to draw from it far-reaching conclusions illustrated by concrete examples. Kapp's essay will greatly assist us in gaining an understanding of the enormous difficulties that are involved in any attempt to show inductively that nature is simple.

Kapp interprets Ockham's Razor as a rule always to make the 'minimum assumption' which is defined as 'the one that is completely unspecific'. By obeying this rule we are not merely adopting provisionally a methodological procedure which may or may not lead to correct results but are positively assured of success. Ockham's Razor is required by the objective character of the laws of nature. Thus he announces:

> I wish to raise it [Ockham's Razor] from a mere rule of procedure to one of the great universal principles to which the whole of the physical world conforms. At this level it would be worded as follows: *In physics the minimum assumption always constitutes the true generalization.*[2]

This is equivalent—he explains—to saying that there is no law in physics that makes for specified order and therefore '*In physics a generalization that is logically possible is also physically possible.*'[3]

Kapp's principle is best understood by examining the way in which it is applied to derive certain concrete results in physics. Here are two examples—

(1) Kapp claims that the falsity of the doctrine that nature abhors a vacuum follows directly from the principle of minimum assumption. He says:

[1] R. O. Kapp, 'Ockham's Razor and the Unification of Physical Science', *British Journal for the Philosophy of Science*, VIII, 1958, pp. 265–280.

[2] Ibid., p. 272.   [3] Ibid., p. 279.

. . . it was assumed at one time that nature has specific likes and dis-likes; for instance, that she abhors a vacuum. This could be trans-lated into contemporary language as the specific assumption that a law of physics prevents the density of matter from falling below a specific value. But it is now known that the true generalization about the density of matter is unspecific. The laws of physics permit any density, ranging from the high concentration that occurs in the white dwarf stars to the extreme tenuousness of extragalactic space.[1]

(2) This example concerns a more scientific result, namely the discovery of Hafnium, the element with seventy-two unit charges in its nucleus. This element remained unobserved long after the construction of the periodic table, but its existence was predicted and according to Kapp it 'was predicted purely on the basis of this principle'.[2] For, he explains, the principle forbidding specific assumptions demands that there be nuclei with *any* number of charges, including the number seventy-two. He goes even farther and points out that it should have been clear that 'any' includes zero as well. Consequently the existence of the Neutron, too, should have been predicted on the basis of the principle before it was actually observed.

An immediate question that arises in connection with the last example is: how do we account for the fact that there are no nuclei containing more than ninety-two charges? Clearly the unspecific assumption implies that there be no upper limit to the number of charges a nucleus may have. An answer to this question is provided by Kapp in the following manner:

> For the elements to be found in nature the maximum number of such charges is ninety-two, a stability limit. This limit provided a logical reason why no nucleus could be observed in nature with more than ninety-two charges, for a greater number would be in-consistent with the definition of a stable particle.[3]

These last words are somewhat puzzling. True enough, to call a nucleus stable when we can see that it disintegrates 'would be in-consistent with the definition of a stable particle'. But there is noth-ing contrary to logic in stating that a nucleus of ninety-three or more charges does not disintegrate and therefore is to be found in a stable state. It is only inconsistent with observation.

[1] R. O. Kapp, 'Ockham's Razor and the Unification of Physical Science', *British Journal for the Philosophy of Science*, VIII, 1958 p. 275.
[2] Ibid., p. 276.   [3] Ibid., p. 276.

We are forced, therefore, to conclude that the only way Kapp could assign a 'logical reason' for the disintegration of such nuclei is by claiming that the laws of forces which apply within a nucleus entail that they cannot remain stable. From this we may then infer the sense in which the expression 'logically possible' is employed in the statement, 'In physics a generalization that is logically possible is also physically possible.' The intention must have been to exclude not only generalizations which are self-contradictory but also generalizations that stand in contradiction to already established propositions. In our case, then, the generalization that the number of charges constituting the nucleus may be as great as you like is to be regarded as 'logically impossible', as it contradicts the propositions embodying the laws of forces governing the interior of nuclei.

This means that the Principle of Minimum Assumption does not apply to all propositions but only to 'fundamental' propositions. These fundamental propositions may, however, entail 'secondary' propositions which violate the principle. We are compelled to come to this conclusion anyway, for otherwise Kapp's law would continually be found flouted in physics. One could ask for example: if the principle was observed by nature, why is there a lower limit below which the temperature of a material system does not drop? The completely unspecific assumption is surely that the temperature of a body may be anything. How do we then account for the existence of the absolute zero of temperature? Or in the same manner one may ask: why can a body not acquire a velocity greater than that of light, when according to the principle any velocity should be possible? But the answer must be that here, too, the propositions stating the existence of an absolute zero of temperature or the existence of an upper limit to the magnitude of velocity attainable, are not independent; they follow from other given ('fundamental') propositions. In the former case the given propositions are those constituting the kinetic theory of heat, and in the latter those of the special theory of relativity.

But here arises a very serious difficulty with Kapp's thesis. Is it really clear in all cases where we are confronted with two sets of propositions, which set is to be regarded as 'given' and which as 'entailed', or in other words, which as 'fundamental' and which as 'secondary'? How do we know, for instance, that we are not to start with the proposition that the velocity of a body may reach any degree, as demanded by the principle, take this as our fundamental proposition, and consequently modify all the other related propositions accordingly (even if it does mean the overthrow of the theory of relativity)? Obviously what we need, before the principle can be put to any use, is a clear description of the method whereby to distinguish between propositions to which the principle applies and propositions to which it does not apply.

Kapp, however, does not think that this problem ought to worry us too much. While he admits that it is difficult to formulate the distinction with precision, he claims that

> Without a criterion that can withstand rigorous philosophical criticism one is still able, in practice, to distinguish quite easily between a broad generalization and a more restricted one.[1]

Against this we may consider the following points which show that the actual situation does not warrant such optimism:

(1) Kapp's claim about the doctrine of 'horror vacui' illustrates how in practice it is not always possible to distinguish between the two types of propositions. He said that the doctrine could have been exposed as fallacious on the basis of the principle which demands that matter may exist in *any* density. But Aristotle, the protagonist of the doctrine, did not conceive it as an independent, primary dogma. He presents it as a conclusion that follows from a number of self-evident premises including the basic laws of mechanics. According to Aristotle, velocity varies inversely with the resistance of the medium. In a vacuum where this resistance is reduced to zero, velocity should be infinitely large. It is, however, self-evident to him that infinite velocity is impossible. Hence a vacuum is impossible.

Thus, even if Aristotle had been acquainted with Kapp's principle he would not have made a generalization permitting the existence of a vacuum, for to him that would have amounted to a logical impossibility. How can we expect Aristotle to have known that his doctrine 'horror vacui' was not a secondary thesis, as it is not entailed by the true basic laws of dynamics as we know them now?

(2) Is the proposition, stating the type of elements to be found in the periodic table, to be regarded as a fundamental or a secondary proposition? Kapp's own views on this matter are contradictory.

[1] R. O. Kapp, 'Reply to Criticism by G. Schlesinger', *British Journal for the Philosophy of Science*, Vol. XI, 1960, p. 62.

At first he regards it as a fundamental proposition and applies the principle to it. Thus he claims that elements with *any* number of charges in their nuclei exist and provides the basis for the discovery of the Hafnium and the Neutron. But if this proposition was indeed a fundamental proposition then it should *entail* that the laws of forces operating within the nucleus are such as to allow the increase of charges to any desired value. Kapp, however, argues that on the contrary it is *entailed* by the laws governing the forces within the nucleus that no element may consist of more than ninety-two unit charges. Thus he now claims that the statement about the number of charges in the nuclei of elements is a secondary statement. The Principle of Minimum Assumption should therefore not be applied to it. Hence there is no basis left for the prediction of the Hafnium and the Neutron.

These points are specific to Kapp's thesis. But the problem of distinguishing between different types of laws in nature is a general one which faces all those who want to claim that nature is simple. Whatever one's definition of simplicity, it is obvious that it applies only to certain laws but not to everything entailed by those laws. Thus an elaborate and clear criterion for distinguishing between the laws to which the principle applies and to which it does not apply would have to be laid down carefully by anyone proclaiming nature's simplicity.

On closer inspection a much more serious difficulty with Kapp's thesis becomes apparent. We may notice that even the seemingly broadest generalizations in physics violate his principle. Consider Newton's Law of Gravitation. It does not obey the principle. According to Kapp there should be *any* kind of masses—masses which attract or repel each other according to *any* law. Why are all masses restricted to attracting one another according to the formula

$$F = G \frac{M_1 M_2}{r^2}?$$

Or if Newton's Law of Gravitation is not a fundamental law, then what is? The Law of Conservation of Energy? No, because it, too, contradicts Kapp's principle. For the minimum assumption is surely that all kinds of closed isolated systems should exist. There should be closed isolated systems in which the energy either increases or decreases and not only such systems in which the energy always remains the same. It is, in fact, impossible to find any law in nature that obeys Kapp's principle.

These, however, are merely the symptoms of a very fundamental trouble. The basic defect lies in the fact that Kapp has not laid down clearly the constraining conditions under which his principle is to operate. And all minimal (or maximal) principles which lack constraining conditions are indeterminate and of no use.

Let me explain this with an example. Fermat's principle of least time is a famous minimal principle in physics with the aid of which, it is said, one can determine the path of a light ray traversing different media and suffering successive refraction. Let us state it as follows: 'The path travelled by light going from one point to another, traversing different media, is that which requires least time.' Stated just like this the shape of the path of light would be indeterminate. For the assumption which would conform best with the principle would be that the velocity of light was infinite. Hence whatever the shape of the path followed by light, it will travel from any point A to point B instantaneously. But of course Fermat's principle has to be applied in conjunction with the constraining conditions, which are: the velocity of light is finite and is uniquely determined by the nature of the medium traversed. The time spent in transit is now wholly dependent on the shape of the path. Given the velocity of light in the various media we can construct a unique course which is to be followed so as to minimize the duration of the journey.

The same applies to Kapp's principle which says, 'In physics the minimum assumption always constitutes the true generalization.' The state of affairs which would conform best to this principle would be that in which there were no forces, no action, neither matter nor motion—a universe in which nothing existed but still void.

Undoubtedly then, Kapp's principle as it stands is incomplete. Lacking appropriate constraining conditions, it is not a principle of minimum assumption but a principle of *no* assumption, which is continually violated by the presence of any phenomena.

The only way out of this difficulty would be to stipulate that nature has certain fixed objectives and that Ockham's Razor should be applied only to the way in which these objectives are achieved but not to the objectives themselves. We would have to distinguish between 'ends' and 'means' in nature. The 'ends' of nature are set but the 'means' must comply with the Principle of Minimum Assumption.

This basic distinction has to be made whenever it is claimed—irrespective of the particular form in which it is claimed—that in nature maximum simplicity obtains. It is always to be understood that maximum simplicity applies not to all phenomena but only to those which are instrumental in bringing about the objectives of nature.

Thus Galileo's dictum 'Nature does not do by many that which can be done by a few', implies that there are certain tasks to be 'done' by nature and that these tasks are executed with maximum efficiency and economy. One could, however, not speak of efficiency and economy if there were no specific tasks to be accomplished.

The difficulty then is obvious. It is impossible seriously to defend a classification of phenomena into 'ends' and 'means'. Kapp cannot claim to know the objectives of nature which are to be imposed on his principle as constraining condition. He is not able, for example, to explain the fact that we cannot have all sorts of masses, including masses that repel one another, on the grounds that this would give rise to an undesired state of affairs, for we cannot claim to know what states of affairs are 'desired'.

Of course these considerations do not affect the view according to which the principle of maximum simplicity is not a rule observed by the universe but something for the scientist to conform with. 'Given a certain phenomenon, choose the hypothesis of maximum simplicity.' The constraints here are set by the data of observation. The 'ends' are the explicanda and the 'means', which have to be kept at a minimum complexity, are the explanations.

But even a claim that nature itself is simple can escape the difficulty provided no maximum simplicity is stipulated. There would be no *a priori* objection on the above grounds to a thesis—like the one mentioned at the beginning of this section—that certain fundamental relationships in nature are simple enough to be representable by a mathematical expression no more complex than f—where f is a given functional relationship. But no version of the claim that this universe of ours is the simplest possible can be defended.

Professor Kapp has admitted that this problem presents a serious difficulty for his thesis and that consequently his own satisfaction with the Principle of Minimum Assumption is not a hundred-per-cent one. In the course of his discussion he then makes a remark which I believe is of great general significance:

> Whether the Principle of Minimum Assumption is valid or not, physicists do in fact often act as though they believed in it, and their action has often proved fruitful.[1]

This statement touches upon one of the points which are crucial to one's understanding scientific methodology. There exist other principles too, whose justification may be questioned. We may even find some methodological principles whose whole meaning becomes questionable after proper analysis. Yet even these may have an important role in inspiring the activities of scientists and influencing the course of science.

3. SIMPLICITY AND VERIFICATION

Now that we have concluded that the claim about the simplicity of nature has not been substantiated, the next step is to inquire what then is the rational basis of the methodological principle of simplicity. Although many different suggestions have been put forward, one deficiency is common to all of them. This deficiency becomes apparent on even the most cursory survey of the existing literature, it is: incompleteness. None of the attempts made so far has succeeded in giving an explication of the notion of simplicity in suitable terms. In none of these attempts is a good reason provided why, in many cases where it is intuitively felt that the principle applies, we should in fact choose the simplest hypothesis. They usually provide the principle with a rationale which is relevant to a set of selected examples while leaving unexplained why in other cases also hypotheses are preferred in the order of their simplicity.

In this section I shall consider the idea that the simpler hypothesis is always the more verified hypothesis and the suggestion that the demand for verification is the source for the demand for simplicity. This suggestion is contained in various forms in the writings of a number of philosophers. L. S. Feuer, for example, argues that the more complex theory always contains some surplus elements unwarranted by actual observation and hence:

---

[1] R. O. Kapp, 'Reply to Note by G. Schlesinger', *The British Journal for the Philosophy of Science*, Vol. XI, 1961.

The verified theory is the simplest because every unnecessary component is an unverified item.[1]

The idea of providing the methodological principle of simplicity with a logical basis through correlating greater simplicity with better verification is an attractive one for a number of reasons:

(i) All agree that it is imperative for scientists to strive continually for the verification of their theories. It is also beyond dispute that the best verified theory should be preferred to its alternatives. Thus if the demand for stronger verification can indeed be made the basis for the demand for simplicity, we could wish for no more solid foundation upon which to place our principle.

(ii) If the suggestion is acceptable we shall encounter no special difficulties in describing in unmistakable terms the predicate 'simple'. It will be enough in each case to determine which of the rival theories is better verified and we shall need no further identification marks to pick out the simpler theory.

(iii) There are some very conspicuous groups of cases which may be cited in support of this idea. The two main groups are the following:

(*a*) We always reject entities or processes the assumption of whose existence leads to no observable consequences. For example, no one any longer believes in the existence of the caloric fluid. To be sure no positive evidence has been produced that heat transfer is not accompanied by the transfer of an invisible, weightless fluid. Only that all thermal phenomena can be explained without assuming the existence of such a fluid. With the development of the kinetic theory of heat the stage has now been reached where the complicating, extra assumption of the existence of a caloric fluid leads to no observable consequences. In rejecting the caloric fluid we are thus using both the principle of verification and the principle of simplicity. Similarly, both principles were used when the assumption that space was filled with a subtle substance called aether had been abandoned.

(*b*) Whenever possible we endeavour to reduce the number of independent hypotheses by replacing them by a single unifying hypothesis. If in Theory 1 we need hypotheses a, b, c, to predict (and to explain) phenomena α, β, γ, whereas in Theory 2 hypothesis d

[1] L. S. Feuer, 'The Principle of Simplicity', *Philosophy of Science*, Vol. 24, 1957, p. 115.

alone is capable of accounting for α, β, γ, we shall prefer Theory 2. Here again the simpler theory is also the more verified one. Theory 2 is the simpler as it accounts for the same number of phenomena by a single hypothesis. At the same time hypothesis d is more verified than a, b or c. Since phenomenon α is accounted for by hypothesis a it may be regarded as its confirmation. Phenomenon β, however, confirms only hypothesis b and phenomenon γ only c. On the other hand, in Theory 2 hypothesis d is equally verified by the occurrence of all three phenomena.

Now, if following Feuer we regard the simplest theory as the most completely verified, then this would seem to have the following corollary. Suppose we have a group of experimental results equally well accounted for by either of two hypotheses of different complexity. Let the simpler hypothesis, H_s, entail, that under certain specified circumstances—circumstances set in the very remote future, thus preventing us from subjecting the matter to an experimental verification—a given state of affairs S_s will obtain. Let the corresponding state of affairs entailed by the more complex hypothesis H_c be different from this, and be denoted by S_c. It stands to reason, that although neither the proposition 'S_s will obtain' nor the proposition 'S_c will obtain' is directly verifiable, we should regard the first of these as verified to some extent. The reason simply being that the proposition 'S_s will obtain' is entailed by H_s, and H_s is the hypothesis which is considered on our present theory of simplicity as the hypothesis borne out by the given group of experiments.

This point is, however, not conceded by some of the leading representatives of modern positivism or verificationism. Their attitude seems to be that one must not grant to a proposition the status of an empirical or even just a meaningful status solely on the grounds that it follows from the simplest hypothesis available. They will not hesitate to invoke the possibility of a more complex hypothesis, rather than commit themselves to any extent to the unverifiable consequences of the simpler one. The approach of these philosophers to individual examples of the general case described above, suggests that they adopt the simpler theory just because it is the simpler and for no further positive reason. It is done on a purely tentative basis. They regard the simpler hypothesis as being in no way better verified than the complex one.

As an example of this outlook we may consider P. Duhem, who

in his *The Aim and Structure of Physical Theory*—regarded as one of the classical expositions of the positivistic standpoint in physics—objects to theorizing about the origins of the universe or to making forecasts about its ultimate fate. For all such theories are based on the assumption that Newton's laws of mechanics are true with absolute certainty, whereas in fact there are infinite numbers of other ways to account, with equal precision, for all the known celestial phenomena. It is quite conceivable—maintains Duhem—that the true laws of mechanics are different from Newton's in their mathematical form, yet the results of the calculations based on those are so nearly identical with the results obtained from Newton's laws, that the deviations between the positions assigned through the use of different laws to the same heavenly bodies will manifest themselves only in the course of millions of years. The possibility of constructing other theories than Newton's, leading to different results in the remote future or past, is sufficient for Duhem, even though he himself admits that Newton's laws are the simplest of all the possible ones, to regard all talk about distant epochs of time as 'absurd'.[1]

Another example is the attitude of P. W. Bridgman, the founder of a special branch of verificationism who, for reasons similar to the above ones, questions the meaningfulness of the common assertion, made on the basis of statistical mechanics, that unfamiliar configurations of a system are only improbable, but not impossible. It is even claimed that one could compute how many years one may expect to wait to see a pail of water freeze on fire. These assertions are based on the assumption that the laws of mechanics are really as we know them to be. But Bridgman says:

> I can see no reason why he should not assume small variations in the laws of mechanics specially and arbitrarily constructed so as to rule out just these rare occurrences, and no one can deny that such is a 'possible' theory if it leads into no measurable conflict with experiment.[2]

Thus the argument that on the basis of the principle of simplicity we are not to assume such small variations in the laws of mechanics, does not appeal to Bridgman.

[1] P. Duhem, *The Aim and Structure of Physical Theory* (Princeton, Univ. Press), p. 288.
[2] P. W. Bridgman, *The Nature of Physical Theory* (Dover Publications), p. 99.

We may also refer briefly to Bridgman's attitude in general to the methods employed by the astronomers and cosmologists. In his opinion some of those methods are 'perfectly hair-raising extra-polations' for they assume that physical laws as they are known to us continue to hold in remote times or in space at vast distances from us. In fact, he questions altogether the assumption that any established relationship continues to hold for extreme and untested values of any physical parameter such as temperature pressure and density. When dealing with stars, therefore, where such extreme values of these parameters are very common, one is not entitled to assume the validity of any of our known laws. Although it certainly would seem more simple to assume the uniformity of all laws and to take it for granted that one and the same law holds for diverse circumstances, Bridgman refuses to adopt simplicity as his standard for the acceptance of the claims of astronomers.

All this, however, does not affect the validity of Feuer's thesis. For to show that the implications of Feuer's suggestion are at variance with the ideas of some verificationists is not the same as showing that they are at variance with verificationism itself. There is no reason to regard even the most outstanding spokesmen for verificationism as the final authorities of what their doctrines are precisely about. In fact, new implications of verificationism are constantly being brought to light. Thus, all that we can say is that the above two authors do not seem to agree that the simpler theory is more verified than the complex one by a given set of experiments which is equally well explained by both theories. At any rate they do not consider the relative simplicity of a hypothesis as a basis to turn an otherwise untested corollary into a verified one, not even to the slightest degree. Feuer definitely disagrees with their views. He made it explicitly clear when these points were brought to his atten-tion[1] that he does not endorse the attitude of these philosophers who without any positive proof to the contrary refuse to accept the consequences of the simplest hypothesis.

Now we turn to the most significant feature of the suggestion to explicate the concept of simplicity on the basis of verification, namely its limited applicability. While it will be agreed that by correlating simplicity and verification an important aspect of simplicity has been revealed, the fact remains that this aspect is

[1] L. S. Feuer, 'Rejoinder on the Principle of Simplicity', *Philosophy of Science*, Vol. 26, 1957, pp. 43–45.

present only in selected cases. The principle of verification can thus not provide a comprehensive basis for Ockham's Razor.

The argument used on page 20 under (iii) b applies only where the phenomena to be explained can be broken up into distinct parts such as α, β, γ and the more complex theory has corresponding hypotheses a, b, c to account for these components. But when such a breaking up into parts cannot be affected, then in general no claim can be made for preferring simplicity on the basis of stronger verification.

To illustrate we may use a fictitious historical example. Imagine that the following took place in 1846 when Leverrier and Adams tried to account accurately for the observed perturbations in the movements of the planet Uranus. Suppose they had arrived at two unique solutions, that is, they had obtained a second solution in addition to the one which led to the discovery of Neptune. Suppose that the first solution stipulated one planet at a given position; the second stipulated a dozen planets of larger magnitudes, but so situated as partly to cancel each other's effect and still give rise to the same perturbation as the single planet of the first solution.

It is, of course, an entirely irrelevant question whether it is mathematically possible to find a unique configuration of a dozen planets to replace the effect of Neptune. The point is that if such a unique alternative hypothesis were available it is quite clear that we should intuitively reject it in favour of the Neptune hypothesis. But here we cannot say that the shape of Uranus' orbit better confirms the Neptune hypothesis than the dozen larger planet hypothesis. For the orbit of Uranus cannot be separated into discrete parts and looked upon each of them as the resultant of the gravitational influence of a different planet. Hence we cannot claim that the existence of each one of the dozen planets in the second hypothesis is confirmed only by a certain section of Uranus' path whereas the Neptune hypothesis is confirmed by the whole of the path.

It should, however, be mentioned that in a very special case one could yet support, on the basis of the principle of verification, the hypothesis with the fewer planets, by employing the argument used in (iii) on p. 20. This is the case when among the dozen planets of the second hypothesis there is one identical in every respect with Neptune. Under these circumstances the remaining eleven planets cancel completely each others' effect upon the orbit of Uranus. The assumption of their existence leads to no observable consequence, and is therefore to be regarded as wholly unverified.

If, however, none of the dozen planets stipulated is identical with Neptune, it is impossible to point at any one of them and claim that the assumption of the existence of this particular planet is superfluous and unwarranted by observation, as all twelve of them jointly give rise to the orbit of Uranus.

We may express this in a general fashion thus: when two theories are available both leading to the same observation, one built on n separate postulates the other on $n + p$, and the first n entities are common to both theories, we have a clean-cut argument in favour of the simpler theory on basis of verification. The inclusion of p additional elements in our theory is entirely unwarranted as it produces no additional effects. And the main point is that we know *which* p additional elements are unnecessary (i.e. those which are not common to both theories). Therefore in this case the surplus elements can be identified and pointed out, as the barren part of the complex theory. But as soon as we are presented with two theories whose elements do not overlap this does not apply. If n is number of postulates required for Theory 1 and there are more than p postulates not common to the two theories, no particular element in Theory 2 can be singled out as extraneous. In this case one cannot argue against the complex theory, saying it contains surplus elements not borne out by observation when none of these can be identified.

Until now the term 'better verified' has been applied to a theory either because it possessed no barren elements, that is, elements which gave rise to no observable consequences, or because it led to more observable consequences than its alternative. The term 'better verified' may, however, be used in a different sense too. A theory may be regarded better verified than its rival because it entails a state of affairs which is more *accurately* represented by the facts. When the expression is used in this sense then not only does the principle of simplicity cease to be an entailment of the principle of verifiability, but stands in direct opposition to it. The two principles act in a way as antidotes to one another.

It will be of interest to read a passage from H. Poincare's *Science and Hypothesis*[1] where this idea is expressed in the following way:

[1] Dover Publications, p. 146.

It is clear that any fact can be generalized in an infinite number of ways, and it is a question of choice. The choice can only be guided by considerations of simplicity. Let us take the most ordinary case, that of interpolation. We draw a continuous line as regularly as possible between the points given by observation. Why do we avoid angular points and inflexions that are too sharp? Why do we not make our curve describe the most capricious zigzags? It is because we know beforehand, or think we know, that the law we have to express cannot be so complicated as all that. The mass of Jupiter may be deduced either from the movements of his satellites, or from the perturbations of the major planets or from those of the minor planets. If we take mean of the determinations obtained by these three methods, we find three numbers very close together, but not quite identical. The result might be interpreted by supposing that the gravitational constant is not the same in the three cases; *the observations would be certainly much better represented* [emphasis mine]. Why do we reject this interpretation? Not because it is absurd but because it is uselessly complicated.

It is generally recognized that if nothing else had been admitted into science but the precise results of observations, scientific knowledge would have developed into a gigantic unmanageable compendium of isolated items of information. Science owes its unity, tractability and fertility to the fact that we overlook the precise details of each individual case, choose to simplify matters by assuming common uniformities and explain irregularities as due to accidental factors. An uncompromising insistence on strict verification would deprive science of its explanatory and predictive power. We produce useful theories only when our demand for verification is tempered by a readiness to simplify in order to unify. The hypotheses advanced in science are very often the resultants of these opposing tendencies of striving for the safety provided by accurate verification and the fruitfulness which arises from simplification.

These considerations show that although in our drive for the increased confirmation of scientific theories we may be often led to choose the simpler theory, this is not always the case. Thus the principle of simplicity is not a corollary of the principle of verification.

4. SIMPLICITY AND FALSIFIABILITY

Now we shall turn to another suggestion of what simplicity is and why it should always be pursued. This suggestion is advanced by

K. R. Popper in his celebrated book *The Logic of Scientific Discovery*. Apart from their intrinsic interest, Popper's ideas on simplicity merit special consideration for at least two reasons. Firstly these ideas proved to be very influential and have been approved[1] or even adopted[2] by other distinguished philosophers. Secondly, whereas most philosophers adopt toward the subject an attitude that is tentative in varying degrees and they themselves acknowledge the incompleteness of their analysis, Popper categorically declares that through his explication:

> The epistemological questions which arise in connection with the concept of simplicity can all be answered . . .[3]

Popper's suggestion forms an integral part of his well-known views on the nature of scientific theory construction. According to these views such construction should be governed by the central aim of producing theories as vulnerable to falsification as possible. The more falsifiable a theory, the more empirical facts it forbids, the more 'it says' and therefore the more it is to be preferred. The principle of simplicity is merely a corollary to this more fundamental principle of always striving to produce theories with the highest degree of falsifiability. For Popper claims that in every case of conflicting hypotheses, that hypothesis which would intuitively be regarded as the simpler can also be shown to be the more falsifiable. Therefore:

> Simple statements, if knowledge is our object, are to be prized higher than less simple ones *because they tell us more; because their empirical content is greater and because they are better testable.*[4]

Popper does not advance a general proof for his thesis, he only produces a few examples in which greater simplicity and greater falsifiability do seem to go hand in hand. One of his examples con-

[1] E.g. J. G. Kemeny, 'The Use of Simplicity in Induction', *Philosophical Review*, Vol. LXII, 1953, p. 404.

[2] E.g. William Kneale or F. S. Barker. Kneale, in his well-known *Probability and Induction* (Oxford, 1949), pp. 229–230, adopts Popper's views *in toto*. Barker, in his *Induction and Hypothesis* (Ithaca, N.Y., 1957), explicates simplicity in his own way, but the essence of his views that the simpler hypothesis always runs the greater risk of being contradicted by the evidence and that it therefore 'says more' (pp. 181–182) is the same as Popper's.

[3] K. R. Popper, *The Logic of Scientific Discovery* (London, 1959), p. 140.

[4] Op. cit., p. 142.

cerns the comparison of the complexities of different curves. Such comparison is relevant to situations like the one with which Kepler was confronted. Given the positions of a certain planet at a number of different times, the question is which orbit—compatible with the recorded observations—is to be assigned to the planet. More generally, the relative simplicity of curves is of interest in those cases where we are given a number of readings, obtained by varying a physical parameter p with another parameter q. After each reading has been represented by a dot on the graph-paper, it is the relative simplicity of the curves passing through these points, that determines which one is chosen to exhibit the supposed relationship between p and q.

It is commonly assumed that a straight line, for example, is a simpler kind of curve than a circle, while the circle itself is simpler than say the ellipse. On the whole a curve is regarded as simpler the fewer parameters in the general equation representing it.

Thus whenever it is compatible with the given data a straight line is to be preferred to a circle on the grounds of simplicity. The latter again is to be preferred to an ellipse, and so on. Now what Popper draws attention to, is that a hypothesis involving a straight line is also easier to falsify than the one involving a circle. The hypothesis of a circular orbit or a circular graph is in turn more falsifiable than the hypothesis of an elliptic orbit or graph. And, in general, a hypothesis involving a curve determined by fewer parameters is always more readily refuted than the one with more parameters. This follows from the fact that observations specifying three points on the curve in question may already rule out the possibility of a straight line but not of a circle. A minimum of four points is required to refute a hypothesis involving a circle. For given any three points it is always possible to draw a circle through them. Again, four points given on a plane may rule out a circle but a minimum of five points on a plane is required to eliminate the possibility of a parabola. And in general $n + 1$ points must be given in order to contradict a hypothesis involving a curve with n parameters. Thus Kneale concludes approvingly:

> . . . the policy of assuming always the simplest hypothesis which accords with the known facts is that which will enable us to get rid of false hypotheses most quickly.[1]

[1] *Probability and Induction*, p. 230.

Now the first thing that will strike us upon a somewhat closer examination of the matter is that Popper has not gone very far with the task of ordering curves according to their degrees of complexity. All he has done in fact was to place the straight line, the circle, the parabola and the general conic into two, three, four and five dimensional classes respectively.[1] Admittedly, according to Popper's definition of 'The Dimension of a Set of Curves', the parabola, for example, is to be placed into the four dimensional class. The general equation of the parabola is:

$$(ax + by)^2 + cx + dy = 1 \quad . \quad . \quad . \quad . \quad \text{(i)}$$

The four parameters a, b, c and d, have to be specified before the parabola is uniquely determined.[2] It is therefore true that usually[3] at least five singular statements are necessary, corresponding to five points on the graph in order to refute the hypothesis that the curve in question is a parabola. But the same is true, for example, about the curve represented by the polynomial of the third degree:

$$y = a + bx + cx^2 + dx^3 \quad . \quad . \quad . \quad . \quad \text{(ii)}$$

or about the log-curve, which is most generally represented by

$$y = a \log (x + by + c) + bx + d \quad . \quad . \quad \text{(iii)}$$

Given four points on a plane it may be possible to draw through them a curve represented by (i), (ii) or (iii). Given, therefore, four points through which any of these type of curves may be drawn, which one shall we choose? In practice we shall probably choose (i), intuitively regarding it as the simplest[4] but there is nothing in Popper's falsifiability criterion to make us prefer (i) to (ii) and (iii). The inadequacy of the criterion is more acutely brought home to us when we remember that in fact there is an infinite number of sets of curves, corresponding to the four dimensional class or for that

---

[1] *The Logic of Scientific Discovery*, pp. 130–133.

[2] Strictly speaking four points determine a pair of parabolae, a fifth point is needed to decide between the two.

[3] But not always. When the quadrilateral formed by these four points is re-entrant, no real parabola can be drawn through them. (See C. Smith, *Elementary Treatise on Conic Sections*, 1889, p. 234.) Popper is inaccurate in implying that a parabola can be drawn through any four points in a plane.

[4] This could perhaps be justified informally by saying that although (i) has more terms than (ii) it is an equation of the second degree only, and that (iii) is to be regarded as more complex since it is a transcendental equation.

matter to any particular dimensional class. Before some means of distinguishing between curves belonging to the same dimensional class has been devised, one is inclined to regard the whole enterprise or ordering curves according to their complexity as something yet to be undertaken.

In the context of actual scientific technique it is possible to go further and dispute even the humble claim that by introducing the idea of the 'highest degree of falsifiability' as an ultimate goal, at least an adequate reason for preferring curves with fewer parameters has been provided. Let us suppose that the variation of a physical parameter p with another, q, has been observed and that a dozen readings have been taken and represented as dots on a graph. Further, suppose that no three of these dots lie on a straight line, but that a straight line could be drawn in such a manner that none of the points would be 'too far off' it. The practical scientist, as we know, will draw the straight line and maintain that p varies linearly with q.

Imagine, however, that we took a very stringent view of the way in which our theories should represent experimental data, and that we were not prepared to assume that the relationship between p and q was a linear one so long as there was any deviation from a straight line by any of the dots representing a given instance in the co-variation of p and q. In this case we shall prefer some 12-parametric curve, which though rather complex, could fit the recorded readings.

The adoption of such an uncompromising experimentalism—it might be claimed—would result in making our hypotheses much more highly falsifiable. For as soon as the thirteenth reading was given and it was found slightly off the complex curve, the hypothesis that it represented the relationship between the two physical variables would be refuted. But not so with the practical scientist. The straight line on his graph constitutes a demarkation line of the margin of permissible variance with the given data. The possibility of further dots off his line does not necessarily present a threat to his hypothesis as long as their deviation does not exceed this margin.

This example would tend to show that in practice the tendency to construct theories with the highest degree of falsifiability and the tendency to make them as simple as possible may run counter to one another. The former would cancel the licence to deviate in our representations from the recorded data, the latter would extend it indefinitely.

One could, however, resist this argument by maintaining that falsifiability is an objective predicate of hypotheses independent of the standards set by any individual demarkation. If the objection is sustained then I have failed in this instance to show that simplicity and falsifiability may sometimes become contrary attributes. But no defence could go any farther and even maintain that they are parallel attributes. For in this last case, the case in which the number of points given exceed the number of parameters in the equations of the simpler curve, falsifiability certainly no longer co-varies with simplicity. A thirteenth point is surely no less a potential falsifier of the complex-curve hypothesis than it is of the straight-line hypothesis.

In general, outside the realm of curves, there are many examples in which falsifiability does not go hand in hand with simplicity, there are also examples where the degree of falsifiability increases as the degree of simplicity decreases.

Not all hypotheses, for instance, concern theories, laws or relationships. Some postulate concrete states of affairs. Now whenever hypotheses differ from one another by the number of physical entities whose existence they postulate, the simpler hypothesis is not falsifiable to a higher degree, but, on the contrary, to a lesser degree. For the more elements a hypothesis stipulates the more complex it will usually be thought to be. At the same time it is easier to falsify such a hypothesis when it is sufficient to obtain evidence that any one of the many elements required by it is missing and the complex hypothesis is thereby refuted.

As an illustration we may here again use the fictitious rivalry between the Neptune hypothesis and the hypothesis which stipulated the existence of a dozen larger planets. The complex hypothesis is again the more falsifiable one. We may choose any of the twelve specified regions in the sky (and some regions are more easily searched than others), explore it, and if no planet is found in it, declare the hypothesis refuted. Besides, as these twelve hypothetical planets are of larger magnitudes than the single one, the failure to sight them with weaker telescopes will also count as a falsification.

It has become clear, then, that Popper has not succeeded in providing a comprehensive explication of the principle of simplicity in terms of a general principle by which one always strives to construct hypotheses with the highest degree of falsifiability. It could not really have been expected that the validity of a general thesis such as his, which is supposed to apply to all possible instances, should be established by merely showing that it happens to be true in certain selected cases.

5. THE PRINCIPLE OF SIMPLICITY IN THE HISTORY OF SCIENCE

So far the point made was that whenever it has been attempted to define precisely the term simplicity and provide the principle of simplicity with a logical basis, the basis always turned out to be too narrow and relevant only to a limited range of cases.

Before one can make much positive progress toward obtaining an insight into the true nature of our principle it will be essential to realize that there are two distinct concepts of simplicity: a static and a dynamic one. As a brief preliminary it will suffice if we say: when simplicity is judged on the basis of a momentary state of affairs, we are referring to static simplicity. We are then comparing the simplicity of hypotheses as they are in the context of a given body of evidence and within the framework of current theory. Dynamic simplicity, on the other hand, is not associated with a given situation but with a continuous process. When the fortunes of two hypotheses have been followed over a period and it has been observed how, relative to an increasing body of evidence and changing set of theories, it has gradually become more and more simple to maintain one hypothesis rather than its rival, then we are referring to the concept of dynamic simplicity.

It so happens that nearly all philosophical attention has been focused on the concept of static simplicity, which is of little importance. In the history of science the dramatic role or arbitrating between conflicting hypotheses has virtually always been played by dynamic simplicity. Once this is realized we have removed one of the major obstacles to an understanding of how the principle operates.

Let me begin by pointing out that in order to compare the complexities of two theories it is first necessary to know what these theories are about. It is not enough to understand some features of two theories and compare them with respect to these while ignoring all other significant features.

In all the noted historical cases, however, where there has been intense rivalry between two theories the full nature and implications of these theories were not understood at the time. Furthermore, the disputants were aware of their inadequate appreciation of the theories they themselves were advocating. Hence the various principles of simplicity put forward by different philosophers as means by which such disputes could have been settled would, in fact, have been of no avail. And although some of these philosophers have taken considerable pains to define with mathematical precision and rigour the predicate 'simple', the results of their labours are not relevant to examples taken from the history of science nor to examples that are ever likely to occur and in which the principle of simplicity would be called upon to adjudicate between theories held by different scientists. For no amount of mathematical ingenuity can provide an apparatus to compare the complexities of hypotheses of unknown or of only vaguely known natures.

Let us consider, for instance, the famous prolonged conflict between the Ptolemaic and the Copernican planetary systems. It is often said that the Copernican system is the simpler since it employs fewer epicycles in its account of the planetary motions. For our purposes here we may ignore the fact to which some historians of science have recently drawn attention, namely, that Copernicus has not really succeeded in reducing the number of epicycles required for his system—his own statement to the contrary notwithstanding. Let us ask ourselves: if the number of epicycles employed by Copernicus had indeed been considerably smaller than the number used by Ptolemy, would the relative simplicity of the Copernican hypothesis have been thereby guaranteed?

The answer, clearly, must be 'No'. For the difference between the two planetary theories is vastly greater than the mere fact that they employ a different number of epicycles. In order to be able to estimate correctly the comparative simplicity of the two theories, one must take into account their immensely numerous implications. Our verdict as to which world scheme is ultimately simpler will depend on what sort of knowledge of the laws of dynamics we possess.

It will suffice if we consider just one of the many reasons why the Copernican system was rejected for a long while. If the earth moved, it was argued, objects thrown vertically upwards would fall westwards as the earth moved away from beneath them. The fact that this does not happen amounts to an experimental refutation of the moving earth hypothesis. Clearly as long as this objection remains unanswered no appeal to the simplicity of the Copernican system can be made. The principle of simplicity can only decide between two hypotheses when they account equally well for observed phenomena.

But the objection, as we know, can be met. It can be met by suggesting that the earth's rotation need not imply the westward fall of projectiles since these share the ground eastward movement before projection and continue to do so even after they leave the ground. In other words, we propose the adoption of the law of inertia. This eliminates our immediate difficulty but introduces numerous other difficulties. After all, it does seem evident that a moving body will stop unless continually acted upon by a force. Aristotelian mechanics which denies the law of inertia seems to be borne out far better by everyday happenings than the Galilean–Newtonian Mechanics. If we insist upon the truth of the law of inertia we shall have to introduce in the most simple and straight-forward cases, retarding forces, such as air resistance or friction, so as to explain why the law of inertia seems to be persistently violated.

Of course, we now know how the introduction of the law of inertia and the other basic laws of modern mechanics have brought about undreamt of simplification, unified the whole of celestial and terrestial mechanics and connected many previously unrelated phenomena. But all this was not and could not have been foreseen in the 16th and early 17th centuries.

The point I am trying to make is that at no stage could one have determined the relative simplicity of the two planetary systems by merely counting the number of epicycles respectively employed by them. This would seem an innocuous enough claim to make yet it is not always conceded. A case in point is Margenau, who says:

> As an illustration of the principle of simplicity, the heliocentric dis-covery has a peculiar appeal because it allows simplicity to be arithmetized, it involves the reduction in the number of epicycles from 83 to 17.[1]

A more striking example of over-simplification is provided by Kemeny in the paper mentioned above. Toward the end of the paper he states:

> Had Copernicus been familiar with the results of this paper he could have argued as follows: the planets move in a plane closed curve

[1] H. Margenau, *The Nature of Physical Reality* (New York, 1950), p. 97.

around the sun. We must consider families of such curves and order them according to their simplicity.[1]

He then goes on to show how by the mathematical method he had constructed, ellipses are simpler geometrical curves than the combination of epicycles and therefore:

> In this one step (of assigning one ellipse rather than a set of circles to the orbits of planets) Copernicus could have anticipated Kepler's main result *from purely methodological considerations*.[2]

This example is not basically different from the one dealt with before, except that the gap separating the Copernican and Keplerian systems is perhaps somewhat less wide than the one that exists between the Ptolemaic and Copernican systems. But it still goes without saying that the difference between the two solar systems is not merely confined to the differences in the number of parameters determining the shapes of the respective orbits. In fact, most probably Copernicus, like everybody else, would have intuitively—without being acquainted with Kemeny's more rigorous method of comparison—regarded the ellipse as a simpler type of geometrical figure than the combination of epicycles. But the fact that an ellipse is a simpler *geometrical curve* does not necessarily mean that it is also a simpler *planetary orbit*. The relative simplicity of planetary orbits is determined by many more factors than the purely geometrical ones.

On adopting an elliptic orbit instead of a circular orbit, Kepler assigned 'unnatural' or 'violent' motion to the planets which hitherto had been thought to move only along 'perfect' circular paths. Such a change had far-reaching implications affecting the very foundations of mechanics. The ultimate consequences were bound up with equating the laws of celestial and terrestrial mechanics; appreciating that the law of inertia applies to both; recognizing that curvilinear motion, of no matter what form, circular, elliptic or anything but straight, is a constrained motion; introducing universal gravitation, and so on. Of course, here again, the precise nature of the repercussions of the transition from one system to the other were not foreseen either by Copernicus or by Kepler, though both had some inkling of the complexities involved in abandoning circular orbits which were axiomatic in astronomy

[1] J. G. Kemeny, 'The Use of Simplicity in Induction', *Philosophical Review*, Vol. LXII, 1953, p. 404.
[2] Loc. cit.

for nearly two thousand years. At any rate, it was appreciated by them that the matter was not a problem confined to pure geometry alone. Thus it is obvious that the mathematical apparatus devised by Kemeny for the comparison of the complexity of curves would have been of no help to Copernicus.

The point illustrated by these last two historical examples is of general relevance. Examine closely any of the known conflicts in the history of science and you will see that while the controversy was raging only a small fraction of the implications of the rival theories were understood by members of either side of the dispute. Rigorous comparison at the time was not possible. Today, of course, we may, for practical purposes, regard most of classical physics and chemistry as forming a closed system. This means that the implications of various classical theories may be regarded as known. We can, therefore, take Ptolemaic astronomy, or the phlogiston theory of combustion, or the caloric theory of heat, or the corpuscular (Newtonian) theory of light and demonstrate in the context of our present system of knowledge how immensely simpler it is to hold these theories than their rivals. But today, of course, there is no longer any controversy to settle. Do we then conclude that while the battle was on, the principle of simplicity could be of no help and now when it could be of help its services are no longer needed? No, the principle of simplicity has played a role in establishing each one of these theories, but this role has been different from what it is often thought to be.

In order to understand this role we shall have to lay aside for a moment the concept of static simplicity which features so prominently in philosophical discussions and concentrate on dynamic simplicity.

6. DYNAMIC SIMPLICITY

'The seal of truth is simplicity' goes an old saying. Great insight is expressed by this short maxim. But like every true aphorism this is compressed wisdom and needs to be supplemented. The essential thing to add is that most true theories do not exhibit the seal of simplicity when they are first proposed. This seal gradually emerges and becomes exposed to our view. I shall now attempt to explain the character of this type of simplicity which is a dynamic attribute of true theories. In this way we shall arrive at a principle of simplicity which applies not to a given situation but to a continuous trend. This principle does not act instantaneously but in the course of a process in which the simplicity of the correct theory asserts itself to an ever increasing degree. The logical basis of this principle is at the very foundation of our whole concept of empirical truth.

A brief example may be of help here. Tom and Dick who have just moved into the neighbourhood are known to be related to one another but the nature of their relationship is not known with certainty. Some people entertain H_1, namely that Tom is the father of Dick, on the basis of vague hearsay. Others also relying upon uncertain sources of information hold H_2, that Tom is the brother of Dick. Let us assume that H_2 is the true one but that for the moment, apart from these rumours, there is no further evidence supporting either of them. There is no good reason to prefer one assumption to its alternative. H_1 is just as simple or complicated as H_2.

Gradually, however, our store of information relevant to the truth of either hypothesis one or two increases. Eventually we may have the opportunity to see these people and we may observe that they look the same age. This fits well with H_2, the brother hypothesis, but not with H_1, the father–son hypothesis.

It is, however, not the practice either in science or in everyday life to reject a hypothesis just because one adverse point comes to light. What is usually done is to introduce some slight modification in the original formulation or to stipulate an auxiliary hypothesis so as to ward off the consequences of the incompatible instance.

The supporters of H_1 will accordingly perhaps suggest that Tom who is really the father of Dick is a very vain man who by various means (i.e. massaging, dieting and dyeing his hair) has succeeded in reducing his apparent age well below his real age. This suggestion, of course, makes H_1 slightly less straightforward than H_2. H_1 will become even more cumbersome when further special assumptions about the unusual type of vanity with which Tom is afflicted will have to be introduced when, after having had more opportunities to observe him, we notice for instance how invariably slovenly he dresses.

The end of this story seems to be inevitable. It seems perfectly obvious to us that since Tom is in fact the brother of Dick, more and more evidence—the manner of their behaviour toward each other; the way in which they refer to each other; statements made by their friends—all ostensibly supporting this fact, is bound to come to our notice in time. Naturally, just as before, each piece of evidence can be 'explained away'. But this means the continual addition of independent auxiliary hypotheses. In contrast, H_2 will unify all those phenomena that need independent explanations under H_1. Eventually a situation will be reached where H_2 is so overwhelmingly simpler that even its staunchest supporters will abandon H_1 as the false theory and accept H_2.

This in essence is the process whereby all hypotheses previously current but now abandoned as false have been overthrown. This is, for example, the way that we have come to believe in the falsity of the proposition that the earth is flat. Not that it was unreasonable in ancient times to hold the hypothesis that the earth was flat; but it has become progressively more and more so with the increase in navigation and the accumulation of astronomical observations. By unreasonable, one means, of course, that it requires a fantastic number of special assumptions in contrast to the reasonable hypothesis which unifies, by the mere assertion that the earth is round, so many otherwise unconnected phenomena. The phenomenon that the lunar eclipse always has a circular edge does not by itself conclusively show the roundness of the earth. After all, it is possible that it is not the shadow of the earth which causes the eclipse. The phenomenon that the hull of a receding ship disappears before its mast, may also be explained by some optical hypothesis. But both phenomena, and others, whose number kept increasing all the time, are explained much more simply once we agree that the earth is round. That is why at one stage or another everybody came to accept the hypothesis that the earth is round, and in doing so thought he has come to 'recognize the truth'. This is a rather obvious illustration of the operation of the *principle of the persistently increasing relative simplicity of the correct theory* or in brief, the principle of dynamic simplicity.

This account of the way simplicity functions in the history of science seems to reveal the major source of the persistent puzzled speculation and fascinated concern with simplicity in science. It was mentioned earlier how people in all generations were captivated by the idea that nature is governed by simple laws. In Section 2 of this chapter we have seen that there are no objective grounds on which to assert nature's simplicity, and various brief suggestions were made as to the possible psychological origins of this idea. Now it seems, however, we have been provided with a deeper sort of explanation why the thought of the simplicity of nature should have gripped so much the minds of scientists and philosophers.

It is a fact that in science a continuous process of simplification is going on. It is a fact that in all the great historical conflicts the simpler theory seems to have emerged victorious. This could be taken as a sign of the simplicity of nature of the universe. The view suggested here, however, is that what we have is not a reflection of the character of the universe but of the character of our notion of truth in general.

The known fact that it is always easier in the long run to defend the truth; that the defenders of untruth are bound to become entangled in an ever growing mesh of explanations they have to devise in order to keep their theory afloat, is a necessary outcome of our very concept of truth.

7. OPEN AND CLOSED HYPOTHESES

Once we become aware of the conceptual bond between truth and simplicity and appreciate the role of the principle of the persistently increasing relative simplicity of the true theory, the ingenious attempts to formalize 'simplicity' seem to become pointless so far as the scientist is concerned. The construction of a rigorous mathematical apparatus to appraise the simplicities of rival physical theories would appear in practice both impossible and unnecessary. Only in artificially constructed cases where the elements relevant to the theories are postulated would it be possible to use any such mathematical apparatus but not in actual cases. In addition to this we do not need any means for a precise comparison. Since the false theory gets more and more entangled in cumbersome stipulations, qualifications and auxiliary explanations as time goes on, sooner or later, no matter how crude our notions of simplicity are, we are bound to pick out the simpler theory.

But the account I have given of the principle of simplicity does not yet provide a complete picture and hence the fundamental objection to the formalization of the concept of simplicity does not apply everywhere. There are cases—admittedly of comparatively minor significance—in which the same range of phenomena can be accounted for by alternative hypotheses that do not seem to have any implications besides the obviously known ones. Such hypotheses we may call 'closed' hypotheses in contrast to the former ones which we may call 'open' hypotheses. When two closed hypotheses lay claim to our endorsement there is scope for a mathematized principle of simplicity to act as an instantaneous adjudicator.

Strictly speaking there are no perfectly closed hypotheses, but for practical purposes many may be regarded as such. An illustration is the situation faced by Boyle when he was trying to establish the law of the variation of pressure with volume of gases at fixed temperatures. He was able to represent his results by the formula $pv =$ constant. The same results could, however, be represented by infinitely many other formulae. Which one of these was he to choose? Here we are dealing with alternative hypotheses of the closed type. At any rate at the time of Boyle they seemed such. The relationship between the pressure and the volume of a gas and the microscopic properties of its constituent elements were not yet known. The choice between the alternative formulae did not affect the state of any other theory. The relevant factors for comparison seemed to have been available.

In situations of this type, it has to be admitted, one can raise no objection on the previous grounds against producing an objective yardstick by which to measure the degree of simplicity of the theories concerned. It should be emphasized, however, that such a task would still be a tremendously, if not prohibitively, complicated one.

Even when the problem is no more than that of comparing of two mathematical formulae matters are not too simple, since we have to take into account different types of factors that are relevant to the degree of complexity: the magnitude of numbers, their irrationality or transcendentality; the number of terms in equations, their degree, the order of the differentials, and so on. The situation in practical cases where it is hardly ever a straightforward matter of comparing two mathematical expressions representing relationships accounting for the same phenomena, is infinitely more complicated.

In order to gain an idea of the distance which still separates us from possessing an adequate and comprehensive criterion for the measurement of instantaneous simplicity, let us for a moment consider a grossly simplified version of the Ptolemaic–Copernican controversy. Let us ignore the ideological, cosmological and mechanical implications of this historical struggle and treat the controversy as though, in the 16th century, the principle of static simplicity could have been applied to it. The difficulties which become evident in this case illustrate the magnitude of the hurdles that would have to be surmounted before the formalization of a practical principle of static simplicity could be achieved.

(1) Copernicus had to assign three types of movements to the earth: (i) Lateral—an annual orbital movement encircling the sun; (ii) Rotational—a diurnal revolution about its own axis; (iii) Axial —an annual conical motion of its axis about the centre of the earth. Ptolemy was able to account for all celestial phenomena without postulating more than one type of movement for any body— lateral movement. Thus when it comes to the types of movements stipulated the Ptolemaic system may be regarded as simpler.

On the other hand Ptolemy had to postulate the alignment of the centres of the inferior planets to the sun, otherwise he could not explain their 'limited elongation'. In the Copernican system this phenomena follows automatically from the fact that the inferior planets move inside the orbit of the earth and no special restriction on the movement of the inferior planets was needed. In this respect then the Copernican system is the simpler.

Thus we are faced with the problem of weighing different kinds of extra factors against one another. One theory introduces an extra sort of movement, the other a peculiar kind of restriction on movement, and we have to decide which one is to be regarded more complex as a result.

When we are comparing mathematical equations there too we may be faced, as mentioned before, with the problem of how to weigh different types of factors against one another. Without venturing an opinion whether we could succeed in devising a single scale on which all the different kinds of complexities would become comparable to one another, one may claim that these different kinds are at least enumerable. We should therefore be able to state clearly the problem facing us in terms of a finite number of statements. Not so with the different kinds of physical factors that may possibly have to be weighted against each other. One planetary hypothesis may stipulate an additional planet with extraordinary density, the other, a planet with exceptionally large radius; one sub-atomic theory may introduce an extra elementary particle, the other a new kind of nuclear force—there just seems to be no end to the types of physical factors for which we may have to account when comparing simplicities.

(2) Let us now ignore all other features of the two celestial mechanisms employed by Ptolemy and Copernicus respectively, and treat these as if they differed in nothing else but in the number of circles required by each for its functioning. Let us determine the relative simplicity of these mechanisms with respect to this single feature. Now it might seem at last that we have stipulated appropriate conditions for a situation which, to use Margenau's expression, 'allows simplicity to be arithmetized'. We shall see at once that this is not so. Mere counting of the number of circles does not even here amount to a full comparison.

T. S. Kuhn, whose 'The Copernican Revolution' is perhaps the clearest exposition of the subject to date, shows that in order to predict accurately the positions of the planets Copernicus had to employ nearly as many epicycles as Ptolemy, and therefore 'there was little to choose between them in economy'. However, if one did not wish to make accurate predictions but was content with being able to explain the conspicuous irregularities of planetary motion, namely, why they appear from time to time reversing the direction of their movement and why the times required to complete their orbits seem to vary from instance to instance, then Copernicus can satisfy one by employing seven circles only, whereas Ptolemy would need for the same task twelve circles.

Kuhn seems certainly right in claiming that this point counted greatly in favour of Copernicus. That is, even though the two systems are nearly of the same complexity when it comes to accounting for all the phenomena, nevertheless since the Copernican system is decisively simpler with respect to explaining the most significant phenomena it merits preference.

This introduces a host of new considerations we would have to take into account before we could formalize the concept of static simplicity. We can easily envisage the sorts of problems which would face us. What if the Copernican system was decisively less simple in accounting for all the phenomena but would still more simply account for the most significant phenomena? And what if there were n hypotheses; H_1 being the simplest when it came to explaining all the observed data, but H_2 being far more simple than any other hypothesis in explaining 99 per cent of the phenomena, whereas if we wished to explain only 98 per cent of our observations H_3 was overwhelmingly the simplest, etc. Which hypothesis should we choose? Before we could formalize the principle of static simplicity a general method would have to be devised for the comparison of hypotheses whose simplicities vary with the fraction of observational data we wish to explain.

8. CONCLUSION

We may sum up what we have learnt about the function of simplicity in scientific methodology with the aid of the following table:

	Static Simplicity or Simplicity as judged on the basis of a momentary state of affairs.	Dynamic Simplicity or Simplicity as judged on the basis of observing over an extended period a process of relative simplification.
Closed Hypotheses	1	2
Open Hypotheses	3	4

Filling in for the numbers in the following fashion:

1. In actual cases of this kind the attitude of the scientist will be to choose the hypothesis which intuitively appeals to him as the simplest. This attitude has not as yet been justified extrinsically. For the time being no comprehensive logical basis has been provided for the rule to choose always the simplest of available hypotheses except that it is simplest to do so. Nor is there any rigorous method to measure the relative simplicities of hypotheses. The eventual mathematization of the concept and the explication of the rule in terms of some other more fundamental rule in science is not, however, in principle precluded.

2. This case cannot arise. A closed hypothesis has by definition no unknown implications, thus there can be no dynamic process, there can be no change in the relative simplicities of two closed hypothesis. In practice, however, a hypothesis will only remain temporarily closed. Sooner or later it will turn out to be an open hypothesis as with the rise of kinetic theory, Boyle's law became interconnected with other theories. Then we become confronted with cases 3 and 4.

43

3. Here, even in principle, there can be no rigorous way of adjudicating between rival hypotheses. In these cases we are aware of the fact that important elements, that are relevant for determining the complexity of the hypotheses, are missing. We have to take up tentative positions on the basis of vague intuition.

It might, however, be suggested that if Case 1 had a rigorous solution we could decide to treat open hypotheses as closed ones by ignoring their dynamic features and by considering only those of their elements which were not interconnected with insufficiently understood phenomena. One, of course, has to justify such a suggestion.

4. The logical foundations of the principle in this case is embedded in our basic notion of truth, that the true theory is more in accordance with more facts than the false ones. As our knowledge of the implications of the hypotheses increases the false hypothesis will become, through our efforts to make it accord with facts, more and more encumbered with complicating elements. Eventually a stage is reached when it is overwhelmingly simpler to adopt the true theory. There does not seem to exist, however, a rigorous rule as to when exactly in the course of the process of relative simplification may we decide in favour of one theory.

2

THE PRINCIPLE
OF MICRO-REDUCTION

THE principle to be discussed in this chapter has also played an outstanding role in shaping the course of science. However, it differs in a number of important respects from the principle previously discussed.

Firstly, unlike our previous principle, it raises no problems of interpretation. We have seen how, in the application of the principle of simplicity, ambiguities may arise from the fact that it is not always unequivocally clear which of alternative theories is to be regarded the simplest, since the concept 'simplicity' lends itself to various interpretations. No such ambiguity ever arises with the principle of micro-reduction. This principle may be defined as saying: whenever it is desired to unify the behaviour of physical aggregates and the behaviour of their constituent elements, construct those theories in which the former is derived from the latter. In other words 'the properties of physical systems should be explained in terms of the properties of its parts and not vice versa' or 'a physical system should be atomized and its properties microreduced, that is, shown to follow from the behaviour of its microparts'. In all cases it is clear what is demanded or forbidden by the principle.

Secondly, in contrast to the extensive discussion which still continues on the principle of simplicity, the validity of the principle of micro-reduction has mostly been taken for granted. Comparatively little effort has been made to rationally justify it.

I shall argue that the principle, far from not needing any justification, is unjustifiable. In spite of the fact that there exists a strong universal tendency to prefer explanations given in accordance with the principle, the principle itself has no rational foundation. The bias in favour of micro-reduction is, however, so deeply ingrained in our minds that it will have to be shown that it is indeed only a bias and not based on external necessity; that the principle is not required on any logical grounds; that it expresses no self-evident truth and is not entailed by any of the recognized principles of scientific methodology; that it expresses a partiality toward a method that is not objectively superior to its alternative in any way.

This partiality toward micro-reductive theories derives, I believe, from a deeper and more subtle prejudice which consists in the universal predisposition to equate physical order with logical order. We tend to take it for granted that the physical relationship of things determines the logical relationship of propositions referring to them. Consequently it is assumed that propositions describing the properties of a physically 'complex' whole are logically more 'complex' than those referring to the properties of its constituent parts. Therefore it is expected that statements of the former sort should be derivable from statements about the behaviour of the 'elements' or 'simple' parts of a material system since these latter statements are regarded as necessarily more 'elementary' or 'simple'.

In fact, however, the logical relationship between propositions is indefinite as such. For logical relationship cannot be determined outside the context of some deductive system. It depends on the premises and postulates of a particular axiomatic system whether or not, relative to it, any two given propositions are interdependent. If they are, that is, if both of them are derivable in a given theoretical system, it entirely depends on the logical structure of that system which proposition will feature among the early theorems, and hence be more 'elementary' or 'simple', and which one among the more advanced or 'complex' theorems.

To explain in detail the nature of this deep-rooted conviction of the existence of parallel orders between the physical and the logical; to show how this conviction leads to the doctrine of micro-reduction; to demonstrate the complete lack of objective foundation for such a conviction: these are my present objectives. I shall first examine a paper by P. Oppenheim and H. Putnam 'The Unity of

Science as a Working Hypothesis'.[1] I have chosen to begin by discussing this paper because the view it represents is a widely shared scientific ideology. There is also the advantage that, unlike most people, the authors do not merely tacitly assume the correspondence between the physical and the logical but clearly state their belief and attempt to support their belief with arguments. This renders the thesis more susceptible to criticism, and it becomes a comparatively easy task to expose the thesis as objectively unfounded.

2. MICRO-REDUCTION AND DETERMINISM

The thesis of Oppenheim and Putnam is a familiar one: the sciences can be arranged in an hierarchy ordered according to the complexity of the entities with which they deal. The authors divide these entities into six groups corresponding to six levels of complexity. Entities belonging to a given level are comprised of entities belonging to the level immediately below: Level 6—Social Groups; Level 5—(Multicellular) Living Things; Level 4—Cells; Level 3—Molecules; Level 2—Atoms; Level 1—Elementary Particles. At present, entities of each level are described by predicates of which some belong exclusively to that level. The entities are governed by laws whose study constitutes, in part, the various special disciplines. It is hoped, however, that the special concepts and laws associated with the different levels will eventually be disposed of, and the various sciences dealing with them be replaced by a single unifying science.

The eventual unification is envisaged by the authors as taking place by the method which they have named 'micro-reduction'. It consists in the breaking up of a system into its elements and the explanation of the properties of a whole in terms of the properties of its parts. The properties of entities of level $n + 1$ will therefore be explained in terms of the properties of entities of level n, and these in turn will be explained in terms of the properties of objects belonging to level $n - 1$. Thus the only science which will remain, after the reduction of all the others to its level, will be the science of sub-atomic physics.

The authors' argument in favour of the adoption of their programme may be divided into three parts: (a) that the unity of science

[1] *Minnesota Studies in the Philosophy of Science*, Vol. 2 (ed. Feigl & Scriven, 1958), pp. 3–35.

is a desirable working hypothesis, (b) that the possible objections to its attainability can be met, and (c) that there is positive evidence to support the claim that it will be attained.

The essence of (a) is that the unification of science will bring about an enormous simplification, and no one will want to quarrel with this. That the correlation of the laws governing various phenomena renders science more manageable and simple is a truism. This creates no special grounds, however, on which to prefer micro-reduction to any other method of unification. The essential prerequisites for the correlation of the laws governing the behaviour of different kinds of entities are: (1) that the relevant properties of the parts be governed by regularities expressible by a group of propositions which I shall denote by P_1, (2) that the relevant properties of the whole be governed by regularities expressible by a group of propositions which I denote by P_2, and (3) that we be able to construct a theory consisting of a reasonable number of premises and postulates (a small part of P_1 and P_2 may feature among them) in which P_1 and P_2 can logically be derived. Whether this theory is of the type T_1, namely that P_1 features among the earlier theorems of the deductive system, or of the type T_2, in which case P_2 constitutes the elementary part of the theory, has no bearing on the amount of economy achieved. The simplification introduced by T_2 (by macro-reduction) may be just as great as by T_1 (by micro-reduction).

Of the arguments of interest that come under (b), one deals with the objection that the Unification programme neglects the fact of emergence. According to the thesis of emergence, when objects of a given level combine to form wholes belonging to a higher level, the new properties that emerge are not reducible to the properties the elements possess when separated. Oppenheim and Putnam argue, against this, that though in practice there are many properties that seem emergent, no one has so far produced positive arguments to show that reduction is impossible in principle. Our inability at the moment to 'micro-reduce' all phenomena should not be construed as positive evidence against the working hypothesis that this will eventually be possible.

Their stand against the dogma of emergence seems very reasonable. It should be pointed out, however, that Oppenheim and Putnam, like almost everyone else who has discussed the concept of emergence, take it for granted that properties of wholes are either emergent or, if not, they are what we now call 'micro-reducible'. But, in fact, the proper alternatives are: the thesis of emergent phenomena (or the incorrelativity of phenomena) on the one hand, and the thesis of the connectibility of phenomena on the other. For micro-reduction is merely one of the ways in which correlation between phenomena connected with wholes and those connected with their parts, may be obtained. Thus, if no theory can be constructed in which both P_1 and P_2 are derivable, then the properties of the whole are to be regarded as emergent. On the other hand, if such a theory can be constructed, then no matter whether it is of type T_1 or T_2, the properties of the whole are not emergent but connectible to those of its elements.

Of the arguments that come under (c)—the positive arguments in favour of the authors' plan—the one based on the theory of universal evolution is of major significance and interest. Oppenheim and Putnam quote the views of a large number of authorities to show that their table of reductive levels represents a hierarchy of evolutionary levels. Whatever belongs to a higher level in their scheme came into existence at a later stage in history. They devote a section of their paper to showing that human beings lived as isolated individuals before societies came into existence; that, at an early time, only inorganic matter existed; and that there was even a period, lasting from five to thirty minutes after our universe began, in which there was nothing but sub-atomic particles. This, they contend, provides support for their thesis, for:

> Let us, as is customary in science, assume causal determination as a guiding principle; i.e., let us assume that things that appear later in time can be accounted for in terms of things and processes at earlier times. Then, if we find that there was a time when a certain whole did not exist, and that things on a lower level came together to form that whole, it is very natural to suppose that the characteristics of the whole can be causally explained by reference to these earlier events and parts; and that the theory of these characteristics can be micro-reduced by a theory involving only characteristics of the parts.[1]

This is a striking example of the tendency to identify causal order with logical order. Let us indicate, by means of a simple concrete example, where the error lies.

[1] *Minnesota Studies in the Philosophy of Science*, Vol. 2 (ed. Feigl & Scriven, 1958), p. 15.

The uniform reflecting surface *ABCD* consists of curvilinear surfaces of which *S* is of typical shape. We may logically derive the value of the total reflection for *ABCD* from our knowledge of the separate values for all the *S*-surfaces, by assuming or postulating that the property of total radiation is additive.

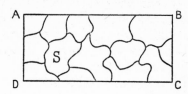

There is, however, an alternative, indirect method whereby we may arrive at the value of the total reflection of *ABCD* but not in terms of any of the properties of its constituent elements, the *S*-surfaces. If we know the reflective power of the kind of surface possessed by *ABCD*, we may use the formula: total reflection = reflective power × area. To calculate the area we employ the simple formula provided in Euclidean geometry.

If the *S*-surfaces are of such shape that the value of their area is derivable in Euclidean geometry, then the properties of total radiation of the whole and its parts may also be unified by the use of our last method. This unification is obtained within the framework of a typical T_2 theory. The theorem giving the area of an *S*-figure would be an advanced one presupposing many earlier theorems, including all those required for the demonstration of the formula, area of rectangle = length × breadth. In the context of Euclidean geometry, that aspect of the complex whole which is known as area is more elementary than that of its physical elements, the *S*-figures. The propositions about the respective values of the total reflection are not bridged by micro-reduction.

Now, no argument from evolution could show that in the T_2 theory the principle of causality had been violated. Imagine that at an early stage of evolution the whole universe consisted of *S*-surfaces which at a later stage combined to form the rectangular surfaces that are now in existence. It would clearly be pointless to argue that since historically the curvilinear figures preceded the rectangular ones, and since the latter were caused to come into existence by the conglomeration of the former, no T_2 theory can truly account for their present properties. The logical order of statements about the properties of different entities is independent of their physical order of succession. The former is determined solely by the structure of the unifying theory.

The argument from universal evolution has, however, a curious suggestive power. I have heard it defended in the following manner: Suppose, for example, that the properties of inanimate matter were explained by a T_2 theory, that is, they were macro-reduced and explained in terms of the properties of organic cells. This would imply that the behaviour of living cells determined the behaviour of molecules. Assuming that a cause cannot act except when it is and where it is, you would be forced to conclude that before there was life on earth—so that cells could not determine the behaviour of molecules—the behaviour of inorganic matter was indeterminate.

But this is merely a restatement of the same confusion between causal and logical determination. There is no reason why propositions about the behaviour of non-existent entities (and if you like of entities that will never exist) should not, in the context of a certain theory, logically determine or imply propositions about the behaviour of existing entities. Our firm belief in determinism would in no way diminish if we claimed that the behaviour of molecules was always governed by strict laws; however, we are incapable of constructing any deductive system in which both these laws and the set of laws governing cells feature as theorems except a system in which the latter constitutes the set of more elementary theorems.

Another significant result of the failure to distinguish between physical and logical determination, and which may be singled out here for brief attention, has been the summary condemnation of some theories as anthropomorphic.

In the course of the centuries-long fight against animism in science, we naturally have developed a strong aversion to anything that resembles the imputing of living forces or consciousness to inanimate matter. In our anxiety not to admit explanations that smack of animism we see the signs of this medieval spectre where there are none. The Principle of Least Action to which mention has been made previously in this essay, has sometimes fallen an innocent victim to such suspicion. This principle, when applied to the movement of a material particle, states that of all paths possible between two points, consistent with conservation of energy, the particle will move along that particular path for which the time of transit is the least (or more strictly, an extrenum). Poincare gives clear expression to the feeling of mistrust with which the principle is generally regarded when he speaks about the molecule moving along the quickest path:

> This molecule seems to know the point to which we want to take it to foresee the time that will take it to reach it by such a path and then to know how to choose the most convenient path. The enunciation of the principle presents it to us, so to speak, as a living and free entity. It is clear that it would be better to replace it by less objectionable enunciation, one which, as philosophers would say, final effects do not seem to be substituted for acting causes.[1]

The principle, however, ceases to look objectionable as soon as we differentiate between the question why something is happening and the question how we knew it was going to happen. In other words we must distinguish between the physical causes of a phenomenon and the logical superimplicants from which we derive the proposition asserting the occurrence of the phenomenon.

In many cases we automatically make this distinction. Suppose we are asked to set up four poles to form the corners of a rectangle and stretch a wire of a given length around them in such a way that the wire may enclose the maximum area. The well-known procedure is to differentiate the expression for the area and equate the result to zero. Here it appears evident to everyone that it is absurd to ask: how does the wire know that in this particular position of the poles and not in any other it has to enclose the maximum area? No one is tempted to say that the wire must have performed the mathematical differentiation. It is perfectly obvious that the wire encloses the area it happens to enclose not as a result of any act on its part. It is only we who know that for a certain arrangement the maximum area will be enclosed and only we who have obtained this information by differentiation.

It is just the same with Poincare's moving particle that describes the shortest path between two points. The particle is not aware of the form of its own motion and makes no decision whether to move one way or the other. It is only we who know that the path described will be an extrenum and from this information together

---

[1] H. Poincare, *Science and Hypothesis* (Dover Publications, 1952), pp. 128–129.

with some other information about the constraints along the path, we can derive the exact shape of the path.

We face exactly the same situation when reviewing the conditions obtained at the early history of our universe when there was yet no life upon the earth. The answer to the question whether or not at that time the behaviour of inanimate matter was causally determined depends solely on whether or not this behaviour was governed by laws. If it was so governed, then its behaviour was determined irrespective whether we constructed a T_1 theory or a T_2 theory in which these laws, together with the laws governing the behaviour of living matter, feature as theorems. There are absolutely no grounds for the fear that we might have admitted final causes, teleology or animism through having constructed a T_2 theory in which the laws of biology logically precede those of physics.

3. PHYSICAL AND LOGICAL ANALYSIS

The next argument of Putnam and Oppenheim is advanced very much in the same spirit as the previous one. It seems to them natural that the physical properties of parts are capable, somehow, of placing an extra-theoric commitment upon the behaviour of systems arising out of them. Thus they say:

> . . . it seems very doubtful to say the least, that a branch B_2 could be reduced to branch B_1, if the things in the universe of discourse of B_2 are not themselves in the universe of discourse of B_1, and also do not possess a decomposition into parts in the universe of discourse of B_1 (they don't speak about the same thing).[1]

Yet, consider the way in which the Boyle–Charles Law was 'micro-reduced' to the laws of mechanics within the kinetic theory of gases. How could this be done, when the Boyle–Charles Law 'speaks about' concepts like 'temperature' that are not to be found in Newtonian Mechanics? As Ernest Nagel so clearly explained,[2] such reductions are accomplished by the introduction of a postulate of correlation, in this case, that the thermo-dynamical 'temperature' is proportional to the mechanical 'mean kinetic energy'. It is a mistake to think that, just as physical analysis will reveal a gas to

---

[1] H. Poincare, *Science and Hypothesis* (Dover Publications, 1952), p. 8.

[2] 'The Meaning of Reduction in the Natural Sciences', *Science and Civilization* (ed. R. C. Stauffer, 1949), pp. 99–135.

consist of molecules, logical analysis will reveal that 'temperature' means 'mean kinetic energy'. The laws governing macroscopic entities are not by themselves entailed by the laws governing microscopic entities even though the former entities physically result from the latter. This, of course, is true even in cases where, unlike the case of mechanics and thermodynamics, P_1 and P_2 employ the same set of concepts. Even the innocuous statement that the weight of a gas is the sum total of the weight of its constituent requires the postulate that weights are additive.

Certain features of common language may also be responsible for our thinking that, just as, say, societies possess a decomposition into individuals so do the concepts of sociology possess a natural decomposition into the concepts of individual psychology. I have already alluded to the suggestive nature of such double-meaning terms as 'elementary', 'simple' and 'complex'. 'Elementary' or 'simple' when referring to physical entities usually mean 'not made up of parts' and when referring to propositions, in a logical sense, they mean, 'not requiring many (or any) steps for the proof of their truth'. 'Complex' too has similar double connotation. Or to take another example, consider the term 'analysis'. According to the *Oxford English Dictionary*, 'analysis' is the act of proving a proposition by 'resolving' it into simpler propositions already proved or admitted. In the physical sense, the analysis of an aggregate is its resolution into its component particles. Both processes are denoted by the same word. Yet we must appreciate that this does not constitute a guarantee that they are parallel processes.

'Speaking about the same thing', then, is not ensured by the presence of a particular physical set up to which propositions refer. It is a logical feature varying with the theories (and their sets of postulates) in the context of which these propositions are viewed. There is no warrant, therefore, to conclude:

> Thus one cannot plausibly suppose—for the present at least—that the behaviour of inorganic matter is explainable by reference to psychological laws; for inorganic material does not consist of living parts.[1]

For inorganic matter may not physically consist of living parts yet the laws of physics may be analysed into the laws of biology within

[1] *Minnesota Studies in the Philosophy of Science*, p. 8.

the context of a theory in which the latter form the elementary parts.

It would seem, perhaps, that one might yet fall back upon another line of defence in an attempt to render the thesis of micro-reduction immune to attack. One might be prepared to admit that there are no *a priori* reasons for saying that the properties of the whole and its parts, if at all connectible, are more likely to be connectible by a T_1-theory than by a T_2-theory, yet one might still wish to argue that it is more desirable that they be so connected. Thus, even though there is no guarantee that in any particular case a T_1-theory can be constructed, its superiority should encourage us never to abandon the search for it.

In support of this last claim one would cite what are commonly agreed to be the essential features of a good theory. A good deductive system, it is said, should have a minimum number of independent axioms or premises that should entail a maximum number of theorems. In a T_1-theory, statements about the behaviour of the elements form the premises, which are but few, and the more numerous statements describing the diverse behaviour of the aggregate are the entailed theorems. A T_1-theory, therefore, better conforms to the requirements of a good theory.

But the unwarranted assumption that has been introduced into this argument is the common notion that physical elements can never have more properties than the complex system to which their assembly gives rise. For an aggregate, it is argued, must at least possess all the properties of its parts and in normal cases some additional ones as well. A macroscopic body, for example, has mass, momentum, kinetic energy, but in addition, it has properties like temperature and viscosity which its microscopic elements do not possess.

This idea, which is perhaps most dramatically illustrated by the perennial search for the ultimate simple elements in nature has, however, no logical basis. One can even demonstrate empirically that it is possible for elements to possess properties not shared by their aggregates. For example, different parts of a system may each have the property of being electrically charged and hence possess a disposition to exert a force upon uncharged bodies. When, however, they are put together, to form a system, their assemblage may become electrically neutral and devoid of such disposition.

Another example: curvilinear slabs have many dispositions

which rectangular slabs lack. One such disposition is to start rolling with different rates of acceleration when stood on different points on their circumference. But, in some cases, slabs which form the parts of a larger system may possess the property of having curvilinear edges, a property lacked by the larger system formed from them (as illustrated by the diagram on p. 50).

Apart from this we must realize that even if it were true that the properties of complex systems were always more numerous than those of their elements, micro-reduction would still not be the only good policy left for us to pursue. It might be feasible to construct an economic theory in which the axioms were propositions about a few of the features of the physical compound. Not all the laws governing the properties of the whole need form the independent, unproven and initial theorems of our deductive system. Only some are required. The rest may be derivable from those.

If, in addition, we also succeed in deriving within the same theory the properties of the parts, we shall then have achieved macro-reduction in an economic and elegant way.

4. MACRO-REDUCTION IN THE HISTORY OF SCIENCE

The conclusion reached so far has been that there are no logical grounds on which to maintain that a T_1-theory will naturally be more readily available, or more strictly in conformity with a deterministic view, or is, for reasons of economy or elegance, in any way more desirable than a T_2-theory. There is still room, however, to take a more modest stand and attempt to defend the thesis of micro-reduction on pragmatic grounds.

It would thus be argued that as a matter of experience the method which explains the behaviour of a physically complex whole in terms of its parts is successful, whereas the reverse method is not. If we cannot as yet find the reason why this should be so, then in the meanwhile, as a rule of thumb if nothing else, we should obey the principle and confidently accept the eventual discovery of its genuine logical basis.

In order to meet this last argument one has to make a study of the history of science and produce examples where the macro-reductive method has been employed and has validly given rise to useful results. After an adequate survey, I believe, one comes to the conclusion that the macro-reductive method, even if it has been tried far less often, can nevertheless show significant results to its credit.

Let us for a start consider a property which we have already used as an illustration of the macro-reductive method, the property 'area'. How do we deal in general with this physical feature of bounded material figures which is called area? Usually a figure is thought of as being made up of elementary figures and the area of a compound figure is expressed in terms of the areas of its elements. When, for instance, we explain why a rectangle has an area proportional to the product of its length by its height we exhibit it as being composed of unit squares, the sum of whose areas equals this product.

From earliest times, however, there has also existed a different approach to the concept of area. Consider for a moment the way the area of a triangle is calculated. Instead of breaking up the triangle into its component parts it is viewed as a part—or more accurately —as a half of a parallelogram. The area of this parallelogram itself is obtained not by resolution into elementary figures and the calculation of the areas of those, but by showing its equivalence to the area of a rectangle.

The first approach is clearly the micro-reductive approach. The second approach, however, which 'reduces' the area of a triangle to that of the area of a parallelogram containing it, is a macro-reductive one.

It is of interest to note that before the rise of the integral calculus, all the methods used to compute the areas of curvilinear figures employed an approach which was not—at least not directly—a micro-reductive one. Once it was realized that it was impossible to find the area of a curvilinear figure in terms of the areas of elementary squares, all efforts were directed toward finding rectilinear figures of area equivalent to that of the curvilinear figure in question. The first striking success was achieved as early as the 5th century B.C. when Hippocrates of Chios calculated the area of certain lunes (figures bounded by arcs of circles of different radii) by showing that these were equal to the area of certain triangles. Eventually, however, the integral calculus provided a universal method for calculating the area of geometrical figures. The method of integration is, of course, a micro-reductive method as it is a summation of the infinitesimal areas of the elements of which a particular figure is made up.

E

Now let us turn to an example from physics proper. Consider the following problem:

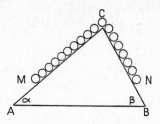

A uniform chain M is placed across the horizontal edge C of a triangular prism ABC. Let the angles at CAB and CBA be α and β, and let AB be horizontal. Assuming the sides of the prism to be perfectly smooth it is required to show that in equilibrium the two ends of the chain will lie on a horizontal line. The problem can be solved by two different methods:

Method I. The first approach is to consider the particles comprising the chain and the forces acting on them. Each particle is acted upon equally by the force of gravity in the vertical direction. But we are interested in the component which is parallel to the side of the prism, for that component which is perpendicular to the sides is counteracted and cancelled by the prism. The component force along the side CA, acting on every particle lying to the left of C, is proportional to $\sin \alpha$. If the length of the chain lying to the left of C is m then the total force acting on that portion along CA is proportional to $m \sin \alpha$. In the same manner we find that if the remainder of the chain is of length n, then the force acting on CB will be

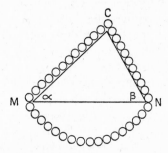

proportional to $n \sin \beta$. But for these forces to be in equilibrium we must have $m \sin \alpha = n \sin \beta$, which clearly is also the condition that MN should be a horizontal line.

Method II. The second approach circumvents the need to consider the particles that make up the chain or the forces that act on them. It starts by considering a different system of which this system is only a part, namely an endless chain lying over the edges of a horizontal triangular prism. Such a system must necessarily be in equilibrium or else the chain, being uniform (and thus one arrangement of the chain indistinguishable from another), would go on moving forever and perpetual motion is impossible. But the hanging portion of the chain is symmetrical if *MN* is horizontal, and it may therefore be removed without affecting the equilibrium. Thus the remaining upper portion *MCN* will be in equilibrium, when the ends *MN* lie on a horizontal line.

This second way of solving the problem is, with only slight modification, the celebrated solution given by Stevin to a similar problem.[1] Stevin could not have solved his problem in the other way suggested here, for the simple reason that he did not have any previous knowledge of the principle of the composition and resolution of forces; on the contrary, it is only after he has arrived at a general solution of problems of equilibrium on inclined planes that he derives from it the principle of the composition and resolution of forces. His ingenuity consisted in his ability to avoid the necessity to micro-reduce the properties of a material system and to avoid the need to produce an explanation in terms of the constituent elements. Instead he succeeded in macro-reducing the mechanical behaviour of his chain segment in terms of those of the endless chain. And he did this within a theory in which the principle of the impossibility of perpetual motion and the principle of symmetry form the primary theorems. Finally he derived within the same theory the mechanical properties of a particle subjected to a variety of forces.

More examples, mainly from 17th-century science, could be cited to illustrate how frequently, when dealing with the mechanical properties of material aggregates, one or the other of the above approaches was in turn employed by different physicists. It will suffice to give one more example, this time from the science of Hydrostatics.

Pascal, in his treatise on Hydrostatics, enunciates a law for the hydrostatic 'Machine for Multiplying Forces' (hydraulic press). According to this law, if forces exerted on the two pistons of the

[1] S. Stevin, *Hypannemata Mathematica*, Leyden.

machine are in the same ratio to one another as the areas of the respective pistons, the forces will balance each other.[1]

Pascal puts forward two proofs. He commences his first proof by establishing in general the magnitude of pressure at any point inside the liquid and from this he obtains the pressure at the liquid's surface in contact with the pistons. Thus he derives the total thrust on each piston, thrusts which turn out to be proportional to the respective areas of the pistons. Each is therefore capable of balancing the same amount of downward force. Hence he has confirmed his law by the micro-reductive approach, for he has expressed the thrust exerted by the whole surface in terms of the pressure exercised by its elements.

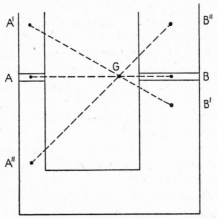

When the weight of the piston at A is of m units and that at B of n units then the centre of gravity is at G where $AG:GB = n:m$. (For simplicity's sake we are assuming that the weight of the liquid is negligibly small compared to the weights of the piston.)

Assuming that the areas of the pistons are proportional to their weights then if A is lowered or raised a certain distance B will be raised or lowered a corresponding distance (the magnitude of which is determined by the fact that the volumes of liquid moved on both sides are equal). But by simple geometry

$$A'G:GB' = A''G:GB'' = n:m.$$

Thus the centre of gravity remains stationary.

The other proof is based on the assumption that a system never moves by its own weight without lowering its centre of gravity. He

[1] *The Physical Treatises of Pascal*, Columbia Univ. Press, 1937.

finds the centre of gravity of the whole system and shows geo-
metrically that when the weights acting on the piston are proportional to their areas the centre of gravity of the machine will remain
fixed if the pistons move in either direction. Hence the pistons will
not move, or in other words, the weights are in equilibrium. This is
a macro-reductive approach; Pascal could have, if he wanted to,
derived the pressure at each point of the liquid surface by assuming
that the pressure was uniform. Then the behaviour of each surface
element would have been obtained from the general principle
about the behaviour of the centre of gravities of complex
mechanical systems.

It should be noted that Pascal's principle is equivalent to Stevin's
principle of the impossibility of perpetual motion. The principle of
the impossibility of perpetual motion as we know, developed later
into the principle of the conservation of energy.

When we look in this way upon the different approaches to the
treatment of material systems in the 17th century, in the way outlined, we can recognize in them the methodological rudiments of
the two branches of physics developed in the 19th century—kinetic
theory and thermodynamics.

The kinetic theory represents the micro-reductive approach to
the study of the properties of material aggregates. It interprets
thermal phenomena in terms of the properties and interactions of
the constituents of material assemblies. Thermodynamics, on the
other hand, is not based on any definite assumptions as to the
ultimate constitution of matter. It is founded on a few very general
empirical principles appertaining to the behaviour of complex
thermal systems.

5 . E. MACH AND ATOMISM

It will be most important for our purposes to understand more
fully the relationship between the kinetic theory and thermodynamics which, from the point of view of scientific methodology,
embody the two different approaches to theory construction under
discussion. It will be revealing to study the views of philosophers
on the relative merits of these two disciplines. We shall begin with a
careful examination of an interesting episode in the struggle between the two famous hypotheses: the caloric theory of heat and the
kinetic theory of heat. We should remember, of course, that the

association between thermodynamics and the caloric theory of heat is merely an historical one. Logically, thermodynamics is no more committed to the caloric nature of heat than to the kinetic, as thermodynamics refrains altogether from inquiring into the nature or 'hidden mechanism' of heat.

Ernst Mach in his book *History and Root of the Conservation of Energy* maintains that the ultimate victory of the kinetic theory over its rival the caloric theory was due to a crucial experiment, the implications of which were misinterpreted. Had the experiment been correctly interpreted, so Mach claims, then no one would have concluded that the material theory of heat had been refuted. He devotes a whole chapter of his book to show where the mistake lay and how it is to be corrected.

To begin with, what experiment is supposed to have brought about, illegitimately according to Mach, the downfall of the material theory of heat? We are told that it was through the results of the experiments of Joule and others, experiments which have shown that whenever work is performed a definite amount of heat disappears in the process, that the idea became established that heat cannot be a substance, that it represents the motional energy of the ultimate particles of the heat containing body.

For originally, Mach explains, the heat engine was likened to a water mill, and heat was thought to perform work in the same manner as water does: by descending from a higher to a lower level (of temperature level in the case of heat) while preserved in quantity. Later, however, this picture had to be abandoned, for it became evident through the above-mentioned experiments that heat is fundamentally different in nature from water. In a heat engine, unlike a water mill, a quantity of heat proportional to the work done vanishes. Thus it was concluded:

> The quantity of water remains constant while work is performed, because it is a substance. The quantity of heat varies because it is not a substance.[1]

However, we shall soon understand, says Mach, how unwarranted this conclusion was if we consider for a moment the question whether what we call 'quantity of electricity' has necessarily to be regarded as the measure of the quantity of a substance.

[1] E. Mach, *History and Root of the Principle of the Conservation of Energy*, 1911, p. 43.

True enough this quantity, unlike that of heat, is preserved throughout the process of work performance. Thus in accordance with the previous reasoning we should conclude that electricity is a substance. But as Mach argues, it is merely an historical accident that we have been led to this conclusion.

For there exists an instrument, invented by Riess in 1838 and called the thermoelectrometer, which measures directly the quantity q^2/c (q = quantity of electricity, c = capacity), a quantity called the 'energy associated with a charge of magnitude q'. Now it so happens that Coulomb's torsion balance, which measures directly the quantity q, and not Riess' instrument was invented first. Consequently it is natural enough that we look upon q as the primary quantity in electricity and upon $\frac{1}{2}q^2/c$, the energy associated with the charge q as a secondary or derived quantity.

It can, however, easily be imagined what would have happened, had Riess' instrument been invented first. Obviously we would have looked now upon the quantity measured directly by Riess' instrument as the primary one and would have referred to it as the quantity of electricity. We should have found, of course, that when work is performed by electric agency the quantity now regarded as the quantity of electricity decreases. Upon this, we could only have concluded that electricity was not a substance but a form of motion, just as we concluded that heat was no substance but a form of motion. Hence, says Mach:

> The reason therefore, why we have other notions of electricity than we have of heat is purely historical, accidental and conventional.[1]

It could have happened by some historical chance that the quantity nowadays called 'heat' came to be regarded as 'the energy associated with heat', in which case the experiments of Joule would not have given us any cause for concern. We could then continue to think of heat as a substance, permanent and indestructible like any other substance, for that quantity which undergoes a change during the performance of work would not be heat itself but only the energy associated with it. The situation with regard to heat would then be the same as it is today with regard to electricity.

If anyone today should still wish to think of heat as a substance, we might allow this liberty with little ado. He would only have to

[1] E. Mach, *History and Root of the Principle of the Conservation of Energy,* 1911, p. 46.

assume that that which we call quantity of heat was the energy of a substance whose quantity remained unaltered but whose energy changed.[1]

Mach's arguments are, as we saw, so simple yet ingenious, and they sound astonishingly convincing. But now let us have a somewhat closer look at them.

What Mach said amounts briefly to this: there are two kinds of caloric theories of heat possible.

(i) The quantity $C\theta$ (capacity $\times$ temperature) itself represents the actual amount of caloric substance present.

(ii) The quantity $C\theta$ merely represents the energy associated with the caloric substances.

Originally we were free to choose either (i) or (ii) but after the event of the 'crucial experiment', which showed that $C\theta$ diminished with work expenditure, it was admitted that only theory (ii) could continue to be maintained.

Parallel to this, two theories of electricity are possible:

(i) The quantity $\frac{1}{2}CV^2$ ($\frac{1}{2}$ capacity $\times$ potential^2) itself represents the actual amount of electric substance present (denoted E).

(ii) The quantity $\frac{1}{2}CV^2$ merely represents the energy associated with the electric substance.

There is, however, a marked difference between the situation that obtains in the case of electricity and that which obtains in the case of thermal theory. Let us imagine for a moment that Riess' thermoelectrometer had indeed been invented first and that we accordingly had adopted theory (i) in which $E\,(=\frac{1}{2}CV^2)$ featured as the quantity of the substance electricity. Later, when we had realized that E is a changing quantity, we should have concluded, as Mach pointed out, that electricity like heat is not a substance. But from here onwards the two stories bear no resemblance to one another, and it is this great difference which seems to have been completely overlooked by Mach.

In the case of electricity, at some later stage Coulomb's Torsion Balance would have been invented. This instrument measures directly the quantity $\sqrt{2EC}$. It would have been noted that the quantity $\sqrt{2EC}$ remains constant under all circumstances. It would

[1] E. Mach, *History and Root of the Principle of the Conservation of Energy*, 1911, p. 47.

have also been noted that this indestructible $\sqrt{2EC}$ behaves in a way strikingly similar to another well-known indestructible $\sqrt{2EC}$ quantity : mass, for it obeys the inverse square law of attraction. This would have constituted a positive reason to adopt theory (ii) in which the torsion balance is regarded as directly measuring the quantity $Q (=\sqrt{2EC})$; and to think of E or $\frac{1}{2}Q^2/C$ as a derived quantity, the energy associated with the electric substance. Thus the development of our views on electricity would have consisted of three stages :

Stage 1. Material-Theory (i)—E or $\frac{1}{2}CV^2$ representing the quantity of electricity. This is directly measured by Reiss' instrument.

Stage 2. Immaterial-Theory, through realizing that E is not preserved.

Stage 3. Material-Theory (ii) when seen that another quantity $\sqrt{2EC}$ is preserved.

In the development of thermal theory there are parallel Stages 1 and 2, but there seem to be no grounds for Stage 3. There exists in the science of heat no instrument parallel to Coulomb's Torsion Balance. All the various calorimeters measure the quantity $C\theta$. But not only is it impossible to measure the quantity of the caloric fluid directly, there is no indirect way either in which a definite value to it could be assigned. Thus if $C\theta$ were the energy associated with the quantity of heat substance there exists no method whereby the amount of this substance can be ascertained. Why then adopt theory (ii)? Why introduce this completely redundant substance which can neither be measured directly nor got at indirectly and which, in addition, has lost its useful purpose as a model. For prior to the experiments of Joule and others, not only could the caloric fluid be thought of as a measurable quantity, but it also played an essential role in providing a 'mechanism' for heat transfer. The mechanical equivalent of heat not being known, some heat-carrying agency had to be pictured. When a hot and a cold body were placed in contact the caloric fluid flowed from the former to the latter. This was supposed to be how the temperature changes in the two bodies came about. But after the discovery of the mechanical equivalence of heat we became aware of something definite leaving a cooling body, viz. energy. Why do we now need two processes when one will do? Why not equate heat transfer with energy transfer? Thus the caloric fluid has also lost its usefulness in depicting the heat engine in terms of the familiar water mill.

Of course Mach is right in maintaining that the crucial experiment did not conclusively refute the material theory of heat, but the point is that it created the conditions under which the kinetic theory of heat became a much simpler theory. Mach admits that $C\theta$ itself could no longer be regarded as representing the substance of heat but must be thought of as a form of energy associated with something. If we think of this something as the material substance of the body itself whose elementary particles possess kinetic energy, we can dispose of this additional caloric substance, since it gives rise to no additional observations.

I have not yet come across any discussion of these points which arise out of Mach's treatment of the implications of Joule's experiments. It is left for us to surmise what the correct explanation is for his seemingly strange conclusion that no reason has been provided by the above experiments for preferring the kinetic theory of heat to the caloric theory. To say that Mach simply overlooked these arguments is not a very likely explanation. Nor would it seem correct to claim that for Mach, the author of the idea of the 'Economy of Science', considerations of simplicity carried no weight.

The clues to the solution are, however, I believe, provided by Mach himself. In another place when arguing against the atomic theory of heat, which in his opinion is an attempt to reduce thermal phenomena to mechanics, he says:

> We have no means of knowing, as yet, which of the physical phenomena go *deepest*, whether the mechanical phenomena are perhaps not the most superficial of all or whether all go equally deep.[1]

The operative word is 'as yet'. Mach was not unaware of the fact that at the moment of his writing, the kinetic theory did go somewhat 'deeper'; that is, was capable of unifying more diverse phenomena, was therefore on the whole, simpler than its rival theory. But as a historian of science he urges us to take a longer range view and not to prejudge the issue. The process of relative simplification has not yet proven itself over a sufficiently extended period to force us to accept the kinetic theory. Mach's approach, incidentally, illustrates what I have put forward in the previous chapter, the way in

[1] E. Mach, *The Science of Mechanics* (Chicago 1902), p. 598.

which the principle of simplicity operates in the history of science. Since the principle of simplicity does not commit us to a certain theory unless we have witnessed an extended process of its continual simplification, Mach is very anxious to point out that there is no compelling reason to adopt the atomic theory of matter.

Mach's anxiety to establish his point is grounded in his conviction that the atomists advocate their theories through preference and not through reason. This conviction was shared by a number of other philosophers, notable among them Pierre Duhem. They argue that *a priori* metaphysical doctrines, and not empirical evidence, was what motivated scientists in their search for atomic theories to explain heat phenomena. The metaphysical doctrines in question derived, according to Mach and Duhem, from the mechanistic world view which permeated all 19th-century philosophy, a view in which mechanics was regarded the most fundamental of all the sciences. Those who shared this belief in the superior status of mechanics were naturally keen to accept the hypothesis of the atomic structure of matter. It enables them, with the aid of kinetic theory, to explain thermal phenomena in terms of the mechanical properties of the molecules, thus reducing the science of heat to the science of mechanics. They believed that ultimately all physical science would be reduced to mechanics. No undue weight should therefore be given to the slight advantage obtained by the kinetic theory over its rival—thought the anti-atomists—when we are naturally disposed to look for empirical evidence which fits in better with our mechanistic world view.

There is, undoubtedly, truth in these claims that the favouring of atomistic theories to a far greater extent than was warranted by experimental evidence was influenced by a biased attitude toward the question, 'How is the thermal behaviour of aggregates to be explained?' When, however, we examine the matter more carefully in the context of various other periods in the history of science it becomes evident that this preference was a manifestation of a more fundamental tendency. The bias toward the kinetic theory so conspicuously displayed toward the end of the last century, was also motivated by a predilection of a far more universal sort than that of explaining all phenomena in mechanical terms. I shall attempt to show that this strong partiality toward atomism which only a handful of scientists were able to withstand, derived mainly from the conviction that the kinetic hypothesis opens the way to the construction of a theory within which the properties of the whole are explained in terms of the properties of its constituent parts. It is again a case of prejudiced preference for micro-reductive theories.

6. THE GENERAL SEARCH FOR ATOMIC THEORIES

That this is indeed so becomes evident when we consider the attitude which still prevails in our own day toward these two sciences. In the early 20th century, and in particular with the rise of quantum mechanics, the mechanistic world view—which made its beginning in the 17th century and reached its height in the 19th century—has been discredited and ultimately discarded. No one wishes to maintain any longer that if we penetrate deeply enough we shall find Newtonian mechanics at the foundation of all phenomena. Yet in those domains of science where the methods of thermodynamics and kinetic theory work equally well, where we have the free choice to solve a problem with the aid of either macroscopic theories or microscopic ones, we give preference to the latter.

There exist today sentiments—the origins of which cannot be traced to any mechanistic philosophy of nature—which favour an approach that 'derives' the behaviour of a material system from the behaviour of its elements. That is, one may admire the ingenuity of some of those methods which circumvent the need for inquiring about the nature of the internal processes that go on in systems, but it is difficult to escape the feeling that these do not provide an authentic picture of nature. E. Fermi gives expression to these persistent and generally felt sentiments when he says:

> . . . thermodynamical results are generally highly accurate. On the other hand it is sometimes rather unsatisfactory to obtain results without being able to see in detail how things really work.[1]

The results of thermodynamics may be highly accurate and arrived at by correct reasoning from the basic premises, yet we are left with a sense of dissatisfaction that we were not given insight into 'how things really work'. P. W. Bridgman also refers to similar feelings and claims they are shared by most contemporary scientists:

[1] E. Fermi, *Thermodynamics* (Dover Publications, 1956), p. x.

> There can be no doubt, I think, that the average physicist is made a little uncomfortable by thermodynamics ... He feels rightly or wrongly that by the methods of Statistical Mechanics and Kinetic Theory he has achieved more insight.[1]

Now that we discount mechanistic philosophies as an influencing factor upon the judgment of contemporary scientists, how do we explain this feeling of uneasiness toward thermodynamics? After all, the explanatory power of thermodynamics is not inferior to that of the kinetic theory if explanation consists in the relating of the particular to the general, the subsumption of a generality under a more comprehensive regularity, or in the rendering of a particular phenomenon predictable on the basis of a universal law. The kinetic theory achieves this by exhibiting the connection between the large-scale behaviour of these systems to the basic laws of mechanics. Thermodynamics, on the other hand, exhibit relevant connections between these same systems and the fundamental laws of mechanics.

Is it, then, that the laws of thermodynamics are not as firmly established as those of mechanics? No one claims that. The basic laws of thermodynamics are just as well established as those of mechanics. Neither is the comparative rigor and validity of the logic employed in the two sciences a possible factor in making one more acceptable than the other.

But the reason, of course, as anyone will readily tell you, is that thermodynamical explanations do not show us the inner mechanism which produces thermal phenomena. It is only in kinetic theory that we are given an insight into the internal processes which are hidden beneath the observed behaviour of macroscopic aggregates. In thermodynamics even if we succeed by ingenious means in securing enough circumstantial evidence to infer from it the properties of thermal systems, we have not penetrated behind the scenes. We have not observed the workings of the machinery, and this after all is the *real* cause of the phenomena to be explained.

But on what basis are we entitled to be so sure that by observing the internal processes of a system we are witnessing the 'real' causes of its macroscopic behaviour? Surely we have relapsed into our prejudice of micro-reduction. At this stage someone might interject and say: 'But will you not agree that you cannot really understand how a machine works before you look inside it and

[1] P. W. Bridgman, *The Nature of Thermodynamics* (Harvard, 1943), p. 3.

observe its mechanism? Can you deny that in order to understand the behaviour of a machine you must first understand the behaviour of its parts?'

This is true of course. But a sharp distinction must be maintained between man-made machines and machines found in nature. A manufactured physical system is invented by human beings and was constructed to fulfil a given function. The inventor of the machine had the perspicacity to foresee that the desired function would be fulfilled by his contrivance. He did this by deriving its faculties from the known properties of its component parts. We too should try to proceed in the same manner: understand the behaviour of the machine in terms of the more familiar behaviour of its parts. For this reason it is sensible to look inside the machine to see what components it consists of and how they have been combined.

It is not out of the question that it may be possible to unify the behaviour of a man-made machine and that of its parts through a T_2-theory, namely, through a theory in which the behaviour of the machine is described by the earlier theorems. But it would be foolish to try to understand the workings of a sewing machine or a motor-car by attempting to construct a theory in which the regularities governing the properties of the sewing machine or the motor-car are the logically simpler ones and those governing the components, the logically more complex ones. For we know as a certainty, from the fact that these machines were invented by a human intellect, that there exists a relatively simple T_1-theory (whereas a T_2-theory either may not exist or be incomprehensible to us).

It is quite different with natural systems. Even if molecules did exist long before they assembled into aggregates and mono-cells existed before the rise of organisms, at the time of our own arrival these things all existed. There is no reason, therefore, to assume that a T_1-theory is easier to construct than a T_2-theory (unless, of course, we spuriously assume that logical and physical complexity always go together).[1]

---

[1] For these reasons it would be incorrect to yield to the tempting hypothesis that from a logical point of view biology is related to physics and chemistry in the way in which radio-engineering is related to the theory of electricity and magnetism, a hypothesis advanced by J. J. C. Smart in his 'Can Biology be an Exact Science?', *Synthese*, Vol. 11, 1959, pp. 359–368.

We may also look back upon Greek atomism, which flourished long before the rise of mechanism, and see how deeply is ingrained the desire to regard the behaviour of an aggregate as the result of interaction between its elementary particles. Greek atomists made heroic efforts to render comprehensible the infinite plurality presented by nature to the senses, through ascribing it to the combined effects of its basic parts, parts which differ from one another in but few respects. It cannot but fill us with wonder when we reflect how the atomic theory was advanced and accepted before there was any real evidence to support it. We may not agree with Mach in his belief that 19th-century scientists should have resisted the tyranny of the atom, but we must agree that the atom did force itself upon the human mind long before its existence could, with any degree of credibility, be maintained.

The atomic theory is merely one of the the ancient manifestations of the sentiments we are discussing here. Those who opposed the atomic theory—notably among them Aristotle—did not oppose micro-reduction as such. But they tried to accomplish it through a different hypothesis. They expounded the doctrine of the four elements. The different combination of the four basic elements gave rise to all the multiple variety of forms.

7. CONCLUSION

We conclude, then, that there exists a universal deep-seated conviction to the effect that just as the physical combination of simples 'gives rise to' physical complexes, so the combination of the propositions describing the behaviour of these simples 'gives rise to' (or entails) propositions about the behaviour of the resulting complexes.

This conviction is reflected in common language. It has also explicitly been voiced by philosophers of all ages. From Aristotle who said:

... the compound should always be resolved into the single elements or the least part of the whole[1]

to Wittgenstein who said:

[1] *The Basic Works of Aristotle* (N.Y., 1941), p. 1127.

> Every statement about complexes can be analysed into a statement
> about their constituent parts, and into those propositions which
> completely describe the complexes[1]

philosophers have assumed without more ado that the properties of
the whole could—and should—always be explained in terms of
their constituent elements. It has been taken for granted that statements about macroscopic behaviour naturally resolve into statements describing the properties of microscopic parts, or in brief,
that there is an intrinsic correspondence between physical order and
logical order.

This conviction has had a tremendous influence on the course of
science. Macro-reduction has been attempted from time to time, and
as we saw, with some notable results. For this reason one cannot
claim inductive support for the view, that even if we do not know
why, macro-reduction simply never works. On the other hand, it is
a fact that the vast majority of theories in science which correlate
the behaviour of wholes and their parts are micro-reductive. The
long history of the search for basically simple elements of matter in
terms of which everything can be explained, illustrates the great
power of this conviction.

The firm belief in the efficacy of micro-reduction, if nothing else,
may ensure that the prognostications of the micro-reductionists
will materialize, and that the ultimate unification of all the sciences
will be achieved only by their method.

[1] *Tractatus*, 2.0201.

3

THE PRINCIPLE
OF CONNECTIVITY

IF the first topic in this essay was a famous and much debated methodological principle, and our second topic a widely known, even if rarely discussed critically, principle, the topic we are now to consider has scarcely received attention in the literature of scientific methodology. For no obvious reasons the principle of connectivity, in spite of its importance, has hardly been heard of. Because of this I had better state it now, even though a mere statement of the principle does not convey very much. It says, 'Two physical systems never differ in a single aspect only.'

Many of the problems we saw arising in connection with the principle of simplicity are relevant to the principle of connectivity problems which will be discussed in this chapter. Here, too, the question arises whether the principle is an assertion about the nature of the physical universe or an assertion about something else. If it is an assertion about the world, then it has to be specified what would constitute a violation of the principle and to be shown that no such instance has ever been presented by nature. If, on the other hand, the principle is not an empirical assertion, then we shall want to inquire what sort of statement is being made. What are the reasons given for adopting it? And again, of course, the most important problem is to ascertain the precise meaning of the concept of 'connectivity' and to describe the exact circumstances in which the principle of connectivity applies. Needless to say, just as before, these problems are interdependent and the solution of one is connected with the solution of the other.

To begin with I shall try to give a crude idea of what this principle is about, a description which for the time being will take a minimal and innocuous form, and with which most people would, I think, agree. Moreover, since the principle of connectivity is really an extension of the principle of causality, it will therefore be helpful to approach the idea of connectivity through the much better notion of causality. The principle of causality will serve as a familiar background to which our principle can conveniently be contrasted.

2. CAUSALITY AND CONNECTIVITY

In most general and neutral terms, and without touching upon any controversial aspects, causality can be described as associated with situations of transformations, that is, with the process of coming into being and of ceasing to exist. Causal links are links across time in chains of events; in short, causes are responsible for changes.

It is also agreed that causality plays a central role in explanations. A phenomenon appears mysterious as long as its cause is unknown. Only when the regular antecedent of an event is discovered, the antecedent upon the occurrence of which the latter becomes predictable, is the event in question rendered comprehensible to us.

Without commenting on the logical status of the principle of causality, which asserts that every event has a cause, one may say that the belief in the truth of this principle has been permanent incentive for our continual search for causal links, something which has paid great dividends. Admittedly, scientists would not have abandoned their inquiry even if they merely believed that not all but some events had causes, but incomparably much greater incentive was provided by the conviction that every event had a cause, and it is this conviction which has played so crucial a role in shaping the course of science.

The reason why everybody has so eagerly been upholding the principle is rooted in the perennial urge to gain control over nature. An isolated 'uncaused' event is unforeseeable and therefore uncontrollable. Causal laws serve to eliminate randomness and unpredictability. Thus it becomes the aim of scientific activity to try to exhibit every event as an instance of a scientific law that asserts its regular conjunction with some other event and which renders it predictable.

All this, of course, is perfectly well known. What, however, is less often realized is that understanding is enhanced not only through the discovery of causal links. For there are connections other than causal ones, connections, the knowledge of which though not indispensable for the predictability and the control of any phenomenon, yet provide a better insight into the workings of nature. There exists a more comprehensive notion of connectivity which embraces not only causal connections but also the connections between dispositions. For it is not only events that may be connected and it is not only for changes and processes that we require explanations. When two physical systems differ in a given respect we do not only feel impelled to say that there must have been some difference in the past history of these two systems and that something must have 'happened to' the one that did not happen to the other. In other words we do not only ask for a causal explanation of the dissimilarity between the two systems, we do not only demand to know how this dissimilarity has come about. We go farther and insist that even now there must exist some other aspect, besides the apparent one in which these two systems differ. There is a conceptual need to look for an additional difference between the two systems as they are at present even after it has been 'explained how' this difference has arisen. And it is this need which comes to an expression through the principle of connectivity.

This more comprehensive concept of connectivity, although implicit in many of the works of scientists, has never yet received any thorough or systematic treatment. Its nature and scope have been left unexplored. It may also be mentioned that our language does not indicate its existence in an obvious fashion as it does with the concept of causality. To the question 'why', an answer of causal explanation is normally given. There is no corresponding interrogative adverb by which the exhibition of this type of additional link is demanded. Yet, as we shall see later, our language does possess certain features that are manifestations of this urge to link differences with other differences coexisting with them in the present. And it is also undeniably true that the discovery of such links does provide us with the satisfying feeling of having obtained a deeper understanding.

But instead of continuing to describe these ideas in the abstract let us illustrate them through a concrete, even if fictitious example. Let us suppose that instead of the familiar property of temperature we knew a property which was like temperature in as much as it was generated by friction and propagated by conduction and radiation, but which had no physiological effect such as the production of the sensation of hotness, and that even instrumentally the only way to detect the temperature of a body was by observing its change of resistance to electric current. Let no other parameter of state be known to vary with temperature but electrical conductivity. Temperature then would be a property manifesting itself in one particular way—the way a body of a certain temperature affects the flow of electric current through it.

First we should make sure that we appreciate that even under such circumstances in which temperature and electrical resistance had the self-same manifestation we would not have been prevented from forming the concept of temperature as distinct from the concept of electrical resistance. For it would have been evident that the amount of electrical resistance a body possessed consisted of two distinct parts. The one was a permanent part depending on the chemical constitution of the body. The other fluctuating part was determined by the processes the body has been subjected to, such as friction, conduction or irradiation. These two types of electrical resistance could easily be distinguished from one another. For when two bodies of the same chemical substance are isolated from their surroundings and are placed in contact, after a while they acquire the same electrical resistance (in current language they are said to reach 'thermal equilibrium'). When, however, two bodies of different composition are placed in contact there may initially be a certain amount of change in the respective magnitudes of the electric resistances but they do not equalize. When a state of equilibrium is eventually reached the magnitudes of the resistances to electric current by the two bodies will remain different by a fixed amount. All this would then enable us to separate from one another the amount of electric resistance a body possessed due to permanent internal factors such as chemical constitution, width, length, etc., and that acquired through external processes. The latter amount could then be designated as temperature.

Now let A and B be two thermally isolated and identical bodies, both at temperatures θ_1 at time t_1 when we make our first measurement. Later at time t_2 we make another measurement and find A's temperature still θ_1 but that of B to be θ_2. Naturally we shall want to find out why the temperature of B has changed, what has happened to 'make' it change. That is, we shall ask for a causal explanation of the temperature change. In fact, if we positively uphold the principle of causality we shall not merely ask but demand that such an explanation be forthcoming, since without it we shall view the whole situation as anomalous, taking it for granted that things do not 'just happen by themselves'. Something else must have happened in conjunction with the temperature change and if we try hard enough we shall find what that something else is with which temperature change can be correlated.

This demand for a causal explanation will be satisfied by a reply that B's temperature is now different because during the period between the two measurements it was subject to friction. Additional satisfaction will be achieved if the quantitative relationship $W/J = K(\theta_2 - \theta_1)$ is also disclosed. Then we are in the position to relate the work W done through friction, with the temperature rise and to foretell with precision the temperature—as exhibited by the resistance offered to electric current—of any system of known thermal history. All elements of chance would then be eliminated from thermal phenomena.

Yet in spite of the fact that each temperature change can now be related to some other event, and in spite of the fact that things have come under our control simply because we are now in the possession of accurate means of predicting the behaviour of thermal systems, some of us could still regard the situation anomalous. To some people it would be unthinkable that A and B should differ in one way only; that the differences in temperature should be disclosed only in one isolated fashion; that A and B should be identical in every respect except in the amount of resistance they offer to the passage of electric current. They would be convinced that the phenomenon of B's acquiring a different resistance to electric current from A can be related not only to an event which was relevant for B but not for A (i.e., B was subject to friction while A was not) but that there must *now* be some additional parameter of state, coexistent and co-variant with electric resistance, in which A and B also differ. Such an attitude leads to the upholding of a wider principle which has been referred to as the principle of connectivity.

According to this principle the dissimilarity between A and B which is manifested in their different reactions to electric current should not only be accountable for by some dissimilarity in their past history but also by some additional difference in their present state. In the example chosen, such differences, of course, exist in abundance. A and B would, in fact, differ in volume, in density, in elasticity, in magnetic permeability and many other parameters which we now call the different manifestations of a rise in temperature.

In general, according to the principle of connectivity, if two physical systems have different properties or the same property to a different degree, this is bound to manifest itself in more than one way.

It seems that on two points everybody would agree without much hesitation. The first point is that since the association of one thing to another is an essential part of the process of understanding, the exhibition of links between the different aspects of nature enhances our understanding. Thus we should want to look for connecting links between all observable features in nature and not only for causal links. Of course there is no reason why this search should be confined to the discovery of associations in pairs. There is no reason why we should be satisfied as soon as we have discovered that a system differs from another in two aspects, and why—in our quest to understand better the nature of the difference—we should not look for a third and fourth aspect in which they also differ. The more connections the better. The more manifestations of temperature we know of, the better we feel to have understood what temperature is.

The second point is that the principle does not appear to be violated by nature. Can one think of any aspect in which two physical systems may differ without at the same time differing in some other aspect too? True, on careful analysis it will become evident later that this question cannot be answered by a straight yes or no. But as long as you stay on a commonsense level, ask any physicist and he will agree, perhaps after some reflection, that in nature there are no isolated differences in properties or in their manifestations.

After this preliminary sketch we now proceed to trace the notion of connectivity, as distinct from causality, through the writings of Ernst Mach, N. R. Campbell and P. W. Bridgman. Each of these positivist scientist-philosophers alludes to the principle of connectivity in his own way. Numerous questions concerning this principle are left unanswered or are not even raised by these authors. In the course of raising and discussing these questions I hope that the character of this important correlation will gradually unfold itself, a correlation so closely allied to causal correlation and yet different from it. The alliance between the two arises from the fact that all physical dispositions imply a regular sequence of a given type of events and that the principle of causality is presupposed by the principle of connectivity, and the latter always demands the correlation of more phenomena than the former. The two correlations are similar in as much as the presence of both facilitates prediction, they differ, however, from one another in that the absence of connectivity, unlike the absence of causality, will never leave any phenomenon altogether unpredictable and undeterminate. Another very fundamental difference will become apparent later and it consists in this: if the principle of causality is ever found violated, nothing short of the actual finding of an event that constantly conjoins the 'uncaused' event will be of help. However, a deficiency in connectivity can sometimes be cured by a verbal remedy.

3. E. MACH'S PRINCIPLE OF SYMMETRY

Mach's views on our topic will become apparent if we consider his critique of the principle of symmetry. This principle has been an important instrument in the laboratories of thought-experimenters[1] and the possibility of its employment presents itself to Mach in the course of his analysis of the concept of mass. He poses the question whether, if we had not yet found out empirically anything at all about the law of gravitation, except that all bodies attract one another, we could have foretold that two bodies equal in every respect will 'produce in each other in the direction of their line of junction equal and opposite accelerations'. Could not this simple proposition be arrived at, *a priori*, from the principle of symmetry alone? No, Mach says, for:

[1] E.g., Archimedes used it in deriving the law of the lever; Stevin in connection with his endless chain lying over an inclined plane where he assumed that the removal of the suspended symmetrical part will not disturb equilibrium (cf. the previous chapter); Huygens and Descartes in connection with the law of impact of perfectly identical bodies.

. . if these bodies exhibit any difference, however slight of form, of chemical constitution or are in any other respect different, the principle of symmetry forsakes us, *unless we assume or know beforehand* that sameness of chemical constitution or whatever else the thing in question, may not be determinative.[1]

We are told then that to declare a situation symmetrical is to say that all the *relevant* elements are symmetrical, dismissing the asymmetrical factors as irrelevant. An ability to distinguish between relevant and irrelevant components, however, cannot be claimed to be based on anything but experience.

To be sure, Mach is aware of the fact that asymmetrical factors are much more prevalent in any given situation than one might gather from the quoted passage. Even if the two bodies did not happen to exhibit any difference at all, if they were identical in form, in chemical constitution, and in other respects, he still would deny that it could be known in advance that equal and opposite accelerations will be produced. This becomes more evident from Mach's comment on Archimedes' first postulate in his treatise on the lever:

Magnitudes of equal weight acting at equal distances (from their point of support) are in equilibrium

on which Mach remarks:

We might suppose that this was self-evident entirely apart from any experience, agreeably to the so-called principle of sufficient reason, that in view of the symmetry of the entire arrangement there is no reason why motion should occur in one direction rather than in the other. But we forget in this that great multitude of experiences . . . are implicitly contained in our assumption . . . for instance, that dissimilar colour of lever arms, the position of the spectator, occurrences in the vicinity and the like, exercise no influence.[2]

Here Mach refers in addition to such incidental symmetrical factors as colour differences, also to more unavoidable ones that may be present in the surroundings. Therefore, it is fair to say that, in Mach's opinion, no situation in this universe of ours (especially if you take into account the irregular configuration of the planets of our solar system or the stars of our galaxy) can *a priori* be known to be symmetrical.

[1] E. Mach, *The Science of Mechanics* (Chicago, 1902), p. 217.
[2] Ibid., p. 9.

Now we are in the position to ask a more fundamental question. What if for argument's sake perfect symmetry were possible? Imagine for a moment two absolutely identical bodies placed at the centre of an ideal symmetrical universe. It is still conceivable, is it not, that they should produce unequal accelerations in one another? There is no contradiction in saying that two bodies, although indistinguishable from one another, differ in one single respect, namely that they induce in each other different magnitudes of acceleration.

Why is there a need, then, to point to the existence of asymmetrical factors, transient or permanent? Why does Mach have to show that there is no *symmetry*, when he could have done better to say that there is no *principle of symmetry*, or at any rate that we are not committed to such a principle by logical considerations?

Clearly, however, there is room in Mach's empiricism for certain presuppositions which enjoy a sort of *a priori* status. The principle of causality, for example, is one of these. Mach explicitly says so:

> ... the law of causality ... results immediately from the supposition of the dependence of phenomena on one another, a supposition which precedes every scientific investigation.[1]

Now the crucial point, on which the whole argument of this section turns, is that Mach could not base his principle of symmetry on the *a priori* assumption of the principle of causality alone. Admittedly, the presupposition of the validity of the principle of causality is a necessary condition but it is not a sufficient one to warrant his conclusion.

For let us grant the truth of the proposition that 'every event has a cause' and also the truth of the proposition 'same event, same cause'. There is still no inconsistency in saying 'if two bodies A and B, perfectly identical in every respect, are placed side by side, their mutually induced accelerations may not be equal'. Sufficient reason could be given for this inequality, provided it is a regular inequality: it was caused by a difference in their 'masses'. Why should it be regarded as unreasonable for A and B to differ in 'mass' even if this difference manifested itself in nothing else but in the disposition to induce different accelerations in one another? After all, even in such a universe it would be no mere tautology to say, 'A and B will induce different accelerations in each other because A and B are

[1] E. Mach, *History and Root of the Principle of the Conservation of Energy* (Chicago, 1911), p. 73.

of different "masses".' For this does not amount to saying, 'A and B will induce different accelerations in each other because A and B will induce different accelerations in each other' but to saying, 'A and B will induce different accelerations in each other *in this particular instance* because *whenever* A and B are allowed to interact they induce different accelerations in one another.' It is an assertion that the difference in the rates of their acceleration is not an isolated haphazard affair; that it is connected to and is determined by the manner in which they have always induced accelerations in one another and in interaction with other bodies, and will in the future accelerate through mutual interaction and through the interaction with other bodies.

But are we not entitled to inquire further and demand also a reason why A and B always induce different accelerations in one another? The answer is that on the basis of the principle of causality alone this demand is legitimate only if a change occurs in the relative 'masses' of the two bodies. Then we are demanding that a cause be found for a particular event, the event of change. But if A and B have always had different masses, the question why this was so, is not a demand that must be satisfied or else the principle of causality must be abandoned. For we are left with no uncaused isolated event to be accounted for.

But Mach would not be satisfied that there was sufficient reason for the occurrence of different accelerations. Clearly because the provisions of links between events does not necessarily satisfy even his minimum requirements for making a phenomenon plausible, Mach takes for granted the validity of the principle of connectivity in addition to the principle of causality. It is on the former that his principle of symmetry is based. Two physical bodies are either identical in every respect or, if they are dissimilar, they are dissimilar with respect to more than just one disposition.

Now causality is indispensable for predictability in a way that connectivity is not. This may be perhaps doubted at first. One might object: if A and B are indistinguishable from one another, how are we going to foretell their respective accelerations? The answer is that A and B *are* distinguishable from one another, through the different accelerations they acquire upon interaction. Admittedly, on the very first occasion A and B are brought within each other's influence there is no way of anticipating what their respective accelerations are going to be. This only means that in order to predict the future behaviour of A and B we must establish their 'masses'. It should, however, not be forgotten that in the present too, although differences in mass manifest themselves in many ways such as density or volume, capacity for heat and so on, we must make at least one measurement before the rate of mutually induced acceleration can be predicted. Only that at present we can make the appropriate measurement through any of these manifestations (e.g., by ascertaining the chemical constitutions and volumes of two bodies respectively we can predict the magnitude of mutually induced accelerations). Thus connectivity facilitates prediction, but its absence never altogether prevents it.

Mach has presented then an instance in which the principle of connectivity—or call it symmetry if you wish—may lead to an empirical prediction. In the example before us we are declaring in advance, without any prior acquaintance with the concept of mass and the phenomenon of gravitation, that two bodies will not be found to differ in one respect alone and they will not be disposed to induce different accelerations in one another if otherwise they have been found perfectly identical. We rule out *ab initio* the possibility of the existence of such an isolated inequality despite the fact that causality in terms of regularity, order and predictability would remain unviolated as long as this inequality stayed constant (or in fact as long as it did not vary in an irregular fashion). It is by virtue of the principle of connectivity that we make this pronouncement.

At the same time Mach points out that all this is in theory only. In practice there is a great limitation in the applicability of this principle. For in practice two systems when tested are never found to be perfectly identical. Some differences always exist between them. These differences may, of course, be entirely unrelated to the behaviour in question, as for example colour differences are irrelevant to mechanical behaviour, and consequently bodies of dissimilar colours might yet be regarded identical so far as their mechanical properties are concerned. But Mach reminds us that we cannot claim to know which dissimilarities are irrelevant and may be ignored except on the basis of our past experiences. Thus the principle would seem to turn out, after all, incapable of furnishing us in advance with any empirical information.

In fact there appears to be another even greater hindrance to the practical use of the principle of symmetry. In order to put the principle into practice we would have had to have tested the two bodies with respect to every disposition they possessed. Only when we have satisfied ourselves that we have done so would we be in a position to foretell that also with respect to the single, yet untested disposition, they are going to be found identical. In practice such a situation can never arise. We would never be sure that there is no more than one disposition in respect of which the two systems are as yet untested. It is very likely that, in the future, properties of matter will be discovered whose existence is as yet unknown (just as most of the electrical and magnetic properties physical systems may possess, were unknown until not long ago). How can we, therefore, ever assert with certainty that two systems are identical in every way?

All this, however, does not mean that the principle can be of no practical value. It is easy to see how, as matters stand at the moment, it may be of great value. Given two systems that were found to be identical in every respect except one: if the principle is valid, we can be certain that there exists some other disposition with respect to which they also differ. Whether or not we shall ever discover what this other disposition is, our conviction of its existence will serve as an incentive to us to make a search for it.

4. THE RESOLVABILITY OF PARTICULAR DISPOSITIONS

In our discussion so far, the meaning of concepts like 'single property' and 'single manifestation of a property', or 'isolated behaviour', 'unique disposition' and 'only aspect' have tacitly been assumed as known. But is it really clear when are we to deem a property to have manifested itself in one and only one way and when in more than one way? Is there a clear criterion by which to tell what is a single type of behaviour or solitary aspect? We might consider some of the queries which can be raised in this connection and thus gain an idea of the ambiguities involved in the use of these concepts.

A and B, the two perfectly identical bodies, will still serve our purpose. Let us place them a distance d apart. Suppose we observe that, after accelerating under each other's influence, they do not meet half-way but at a distance x from A's original position and a distance y from B's. The following questions may be posed:

(a) Suppose we separate A and B, and place them this time a distance $2d$ apart, and find that the point at which they now meet is at distances $2x$ and $2y$ from the original positions of A and B respectively. Next we place them a distance $3d$ apart and observe that their eventual meeting point is at distances $3x$ and $3y$ from their respective starting points, and so on.

We may now ask: are the results of these separate experiments to be considered as one and the same manifestation of the fact that the masses of A and B are in the ratio of $y:x$? Or should these perhaps be regarded as distinct from one another? After all, the initial distances apart, the total distances travelled, the velocities and times at which they travelled were all different in each case. Furthermore, the results of the first, second and third experiments are independent and do not follow logically from one another. It would have been neither contrary to logic nor to common intuition, to find that the relative masses of material bodies vary with their distances apart.

Therefore, it might be argued that the set of events consisting in the meeting of A and B at a point x and y from their respective starting points, whenever they are initially separated by a distance d, is quite distinct from another set of events which consists in the repeated meeting of these bodies at a certain point whenever their original distances apart is some fixed magnitude, other than d.

Thus it might be argued that the perfectly identical A and B which exhibit no other dissimilarities in their behaviour than inducing in one another accelerations of different magnitudes, do not really differ in one way only. As we have seen, their differences might be considered to be manifested in many ways and hence we may not be bound by the principle of connectivity to look for additional dissimilarities.

(b) If, in spite of the above considerations, we look upon the results of the separate experiments as the very same manifestation of a dissimilarity, we may then ask, what if we substitute a new body C instead of B? Imagine that we have performed the same experiments as under (a), but now with C in place of B, and have found that the ratios of the final distances travelled by A and C are always as x' to y', i.e., that their relative masses are as y' to x'.

Thus we have conducted two distinct series of experiments—one to investigate the behaviour of A when in interaction with B, and the other when in interaction with C. It might as well be noted that it has been pointed out—this time by Mach himself[1]—that there is

[1] *Science of Mechanics*, p. 219.

no necessary connection between the results of the two sets of experiments. The relationship between the masses A and B was independent of the relationship between the masses of A and C, the latter could not with certainty be derived even if we know the relationship between the masses of B and C. For we do not know *a priori* that mass relationships are transitive. It is possible for instance, Mach explains, that the masses of A and B are equal and the masses of B and C are equal, yet the masses of A and C are not equal. Are then the series of results obtained under (a) and under (b) still to be considered as a single manifestation of mass?

(c) If the answer to our last question is still in the affirmative, then we may ask the following: what if we were to determine the relative masses of A and B in an entirely different way not involving the measurement of accelerations, for example, by attaching A and B in succession, to the free end of a spring balance and subjecting them in each case to the same gravitational force, observing the respective amounts of extensions produced. In other words we compared their masses through comparing their weight by a spring balance. If we then found the ratio of the extensions of the spring balance to be $y:x$ would this count as a separate manifestation that the ratio of the masses was $y:x$ and would the principle of connectivity now be satisfied?

Mach provides no answer to any of these questions. One might perhaps want to claim that his treatment implies that the results under (a), (b) and (c) are to be regarded as the same manifestation of mass. It is not very important to argue this point. I cited the difficulties involved in the case of mass in order to illustrate a general problem. What is needed is not a ruling in this or any other individual case but the laying down of a comprehensive criterion whereby we can decide in each particular case whether a group of observations are or are not to be regarded as comprising different phenomena. This has not yet been done, as far as I know, by anyone. However, N. R. Campbell—who as we shall see in the next section holds a principle resembling ours—acknowledges at least the existence of the problem.

Let me just indicate first briefly what arguments might be adduced for claiming that the results of (a), (b) and (c) should be considered as a manifestation of a single aspect of mass.

(a) From the results of our experiments performed for an initial distance d between A and B we cannot foretell with certainty where they will meet when separated originally by a distance 2*d*. There are, however, certain things that we do take for granted. We do presuppose that the behaviour of masses when separated 2*d* bears *some relationship* to the case when they are separated by *d*. For the supposition of the existence of regularity and order among phenomena is one that precedes experience. On the other hand, that this relationship is the simplest possible one—namely that the ratio of induced accelerations is constant and independent of the original distances apart—is not taken for granted by an empiricist.

Thus the resulting accelerations for different initial distances apart are not independent as they are presumed to be related somehow. From our experiments we expect to learn how.

The results of the different experiments under (*a*) are not, therefore, considered as different manifestations of mass.

(*b*) The arguments used above cannot be used in this connection, for if we do not presuppose the transitivity of the mass relationship between *a*, *b* and *c*, then the interaction of *a* and *b* is independent of the interaction of *a* and *c*. Nevertheless it can be claimed that the way *a* and *c* act upon one another though not predictable is not a new manifestation of mass. True enough, *c* is a different body from *b*, but what we *measure* in both cases is the same—it is acceleration. Thus concentrating on the operational aspect of the situation, *a*'s acceleration whether induced by *b* or by *c* is one and the same phenomenon.

(*c*) The measurements involved when *a* and *b* are allowed to accelerate toward one another through their mutual attraction are different from the measurements involved when both are suspended by springs whose extensions we observe. Thus the arguments used in (*b*) do not apply here. To produce a convincing explanation of why the result of the two experiments are not really different, would not be such an easy task. We might attempt to argue that in both cases mass manifests itself in the form of force. The two results exhibited two manifestations of force, force as an accelerating agent and force as a cause of the extension of a spring. But mass manifests itself through a single phenomenon only— the phenomenon of force. Such an argument, of course, would involve showing that force could be defined independently of mass.

It follows from all this that the term 'single aspect' does not stand for a sharply defined concept. It is not definitely clear what constitutes a 'single type of behaviour' or a 'single manifestation of a property' or 'a single disposition'. We have analysed only one case, but it is easy to imagine how similar difficulties might be raised in other cases.

Let us return for a moment to the concept of temperature considered in the previous section, which consisted of one disposition alone, the disposition to offer a certain resistance to electric current. A 'heated' body offered a different resistance to electric current than an 'unheated' one. A number of ambiguities could be shown to be involved here as well, but in this case we shall confine our attention just to one of the problems.

As we have already mentioned before, when bodies of different temperatures are placed side by side there is a heat flow in the direction of the body of the lower temperature. Hence it might be argued that the concept temperature stands for two distinct dispositions— (*a*) the disposition to offer a certain resistance to electric current, (*b*) the disposition to alter the temperature of other bodies.

On the other hand, it might be maintained that (*a*) and (*b*) amount to the same thing. After all, what does it mean 'to alter the temperature of other bodies'? How do we know that the temperature of other bodies has changed? By a measurement of their electric resistance. Thus ultimately there is only one way through which temperature manifests itself—through electric resistance. The foregoing discussion shows that the statement 'two physical systems never differ from one another in one aspect only' is an indeterminate statement. It will remain an indeterminate statement as long as we are not given a clear, detailed and generally applicable definition of what constitutes a single aspect. Until such a definition is given, we cannot attempt to investigate the question of the empirical truth of the principle. If anyone were to tell us that he found two systems that differed from one another in a single aspect only, it would always seem possible from the foregoing discussion to point out to him that what appeared as a single aspect can in fact be broken up into two or more different aspects.

Have we then come to a dead end and do we have to conclude that the principle is devoid of any significance simply because we do not know what it means? N. R. Campbell, whose principle of symmetrical uniform association we shall consider next, indicates a way out. His treatment suggests that even if it were true that due to the resolvability of dispositions, the concept of a single disposition is of indeterminate meaning, the principle of connectivity may yet retain a substantial significance.

Campbell, unlike Mach, speaks of different substances which may not differ in one respect alone and not of physical systems in general. Also, he refers to what one may call 'substance characterizing dispositions' and not just to any disposition.

In the relevant passages of his *Physics: the Elements*, Campbell points out that not all the laws in physics express causal relationships. Thus 'silver exists' is a statement of a law in physics, but does not refer to causal links. What may then be said to be characteristically common to all laws? In Campbell's opinion it is, that all of them express the uniform association of some observables. 'Force causes extension' is a law of nature and it is an expression of a uniform association that exists between force and extension. 'Silver exists' too is a law, for it expresses the uniform association between all the other observed properties of silver and, say, its solubility in nitric acid. The statement 'silver exists' asserts that if you have a substance possessing all the other properties of silver it will also be soluble in nitric acid.

Campbell then goes on to inquire whether this uniform association is always a symmetrical one, that is, if a law states that whenever *a* then *b*, is it also true that whenever *b* then *a*? It is true for instance that whenever force is applied to an elastic body, it expands. But is it also true that whenever an extension of a body occurs force must have been applied to it? He answers that if we make sufficient qualifications such as 'provided that there is no increase in temperature' and so on, it can be made true that whenever extension occurs there is always a force. How about 'silver exists'? Surely not everything that is soluble in nitric acid is silver? However, Campbell remarks:

. . . a redistribution of the terms may lead to a symmetrical dual relation; for if two collections of properties $a, b, c, d \ldots x, y, z, u \ldots$ can be found such that each collection is characteristic of silver and possessed by no other element, then it will be true that if one collection is observed the other can be observed; if the relation asserted by the law 'silver exists' is taken to be the relation between these two collections, then it will be symmetrical.

Now this division will always be possible unless there are two substances which are distinguished by one property and one property only; so long as there are at least two properties in which a substance differs from any other substance it is always possible to place one of these properties in one collection and the other in the other; each of these collections will then be characteristic of one substance alone and each will therefore be uniformly associated with the other.[1]

Thus the question whether we can say that the common characteristic of all laws is that they express symmetrical relationships resolves itself into the question whether two substances can differ in one single property. Campbell says:

If we propose to answer this question in the affirmative it would be necessary to consider very carefully what we mean by a single property, but since in spite of a tendency at first sight to admit that there might be such substances, it seems that the answer must be in the negative, there is no such necessity.[2]

Thus Campbell, in developing the idea of connectivity that goes beyond those of events, mentions the problem of the vagueness of the term 'single property'. He maintains, however, that this does not prevent us from making a definite assertion that two substances differing in one property alone do *not* exist. Probably because if we did find an instance that would seem to violate this principle we could always break up the ostensibly single property into more elementary ones as discussed in the previous section. Yet on the other hand the principle does not seem to be regarded by Campbell as a trivial one that can always be safeguarded by simply deciding that what appeared at first sight a single property can upon analysis be shown a complex one, for he also appears to be bringing empirical evidence in support of his thesis:

Isomers differ not only in their chemical reactions but also in their melting points, solubilities and so forth. Isotopes differ not only in their parentage and products but also in the range of the rays they emit.[3]

[1] N. R. Campbell, 'Foundations of Science' (*Physics: The Elements*) (Dover, 1957), p. 75.
[2] Ibid.   [3] Ibid., p. 76.

He did not really need to say this for even if isomers differed in their melting points but not in their chemical reactions, melting point alone may be exhibited as a complex property; it is the property of becoming liquefied at a certain temperature but also the property of discontinuously assuming a different specific heat at the very same temperature.

But Campbell does not propose to spend much time on analysing this point. He is not particularly anxious to clarify whether his principle is based on empirical or conventional linguistic foundations. Immediately after this he suggests a different verbal device which again may rectify any situation in which the principle seems to have been violated:

> Suppose, for example, that the products of chlorinating phenol differed in nothing but their melting point. Then it might be possible to separate out three parts from chlorinated mixture; but when they were examined they would all prove the same. I think we should prefer to deny that a pure substance had always a constant melting point rather than to imagine three different substances; in order to speak of three different substances we require two different properties, one to separate them and the other to distinguish them when separated.[1]

The principle now becomes true by definition for two material systems will not be spoken of as of two substances if they differ in one property alone. The reason offered by Campbell for the adoption of such a linguistic rule is not a very compelling one. After all, it is possible both to 'separate' and 'distinguish' substances by one and the same property. The main significance of his argument lies in the fact that it introduces explicitly the idea that a principle asserting the association of different dispositions may perhaps not be a statement about the nature of the physical world but a rule of scientific language.

Campbell clearly points the way in which the more general principle of connectivity might be significantly reformulated. Scientists, it could be said, will never speak of two physical systems as differing in one disposition alone. It will, however, be noticed that this last verbal device cannot be applied to safeguard the broader principle referring to all dispositions but only to substance defining one. Two

[1] N. R. Campbell, 'Foundations of Science' (*Physics: The Elements*) (Dover, 1957), p. 76.

physical systems (as distinct from two 'substances') cannot be spoken of as one if in fact they are not; that is if they are distinct spatially. Thus if we were to find two systems differing in one aspect only, we could not find the remedy in declaring them to be one and the same system. Such adjustment can only be made with 'substances'. But the first device of declaring a seemingly single difference, a complex one, may be applied in every case.

P. W. Bridgman, an enthusiastic supporter of the principle, seems to advocate this although he does not quite say so explicitly.

6. P. W. BRIDGMAN'S PRINCIPLE OF ESSENTIAL CONNECTIVITY

Bridgman is the most unreservedly outspoken on the great significance of the principle of connectivity (which he calls the principle of essential connectivity). He says:

> . . . the thesis of essential connectivity . . . is perhaps the broadest we have: it is the thesis that differences between the behaviour of systems do not occur isolated but are associated with other differences. It is essentially the same thesis as that already mentioned in connection with 'explanation', namely that it is possible to correlate any of the phenomena of nature with other phenomena.
>
> If now the connectivity or correlation between phenomena is of a special kind, we have a causal connection; namely, if whenever we arbitrarily impress event A on a system we find that event B always occurs, whereas if we had not impressed A, B would not have occurred, then we say that A is the cause of B . . .[1]

Yet Bridgman neither attempts to justify the principle nor to indicate its exact nature and status. The only other place in his writings, to my knowledge, where he again makes an explicit reference to it, is in his discussion of whether we may speak of a beam of light as something that is 'travelling'.

The question he poses is: does light *really* travel? When a thing is 'really' travelling one can detect it in the intermediate stages of its course. When a ball is thrown, for instance, it can be seen and the rush of air can be heard during its flight.

> But the beam of light is entirely different. The only way we can obtain physical evidence of the intermediate existence of the beam is

[1] P. W. Bridgman, *The Logic of Modern Physics* (Macmillan, 1954), p. 83.

by interposing some sort of a screen, and this act destroys just that part of the beam whose existence we have thereby detected. There is no physical phenomenon whatever by which light may be detected apart from the phenomenon of the source and the sink (understanding that the mirror is included in the idea of sink); that is, no phenomenon exists independent of the phenomenon which led to the invention of a thing travelling.[1]

Finally, however, Bridgman produces a novel argument in favour of the idea of light as 'really' something that travels, an argument which in his opinion is:

... perhaps the strongest that can be advanced for the view that light is a thing travelling ...[2]

and which runs as follows:

Let us imagine two identical systems each consisting of source of light provided with a shutter to be opened and closed at will; a reflecting mirror placed at a distance from the source and a receiving screen at which the light returning from the mirror is ultimately absorbed. A light signal is flashed from the first systems source on to its screen via the mirror. One second later the same is repeated with the other system. Later, if we examine the two light sources and mirrors we shall find no traces of the flashes emitted or reflected or rather that these were emitted at different times. For even if a thorough measurement of the energy or momentum of the mirror could reveal whether a light flash had been reflected, it cannot, Bridgman claims, reveal when it has been reflected. Thus the most scrupulous examination of the two systems will discover not the slightest difference between them. But there is a definite difference in the times of the emissions and the reflections of the flashes that took place in the two systems. Can it then be possible that in every other respect the two systems are identical? This is unacceptable, says Bridgman, for:

This violates what we have suggested might be regarded as the cardinal and most general principle of all physics, the principle of essential connectivity which states that differences between two systems must be associated with other differences. A most obvious and simple way of maintaining our principle is merely to point out that the system really included more than we investigated; the

[1] P. W. Bridgman, *The Logic of Modern Physics* (Macmillan, 1954), pp. 152–153. [2] Ibid., p. 158.

93

system properly consists of source, mirror, screen and all inter-mediate space so that if we had examined intermediate space we would have found light there in different positions in the two systems, thus correlating with the differences in subsequent history.[1]

What Bridgman had in mind was this: we know of course that the existence of a light beam at any point on its journey can be detected by the interposition of some opaque object. Such operations, however,

> . . . destroys just that part of the beam whose existence we have thereby detected . . .[2]

and we may therefore be inclined to dismiss it as an irrelevant opera-tion incapable of lending an 'operationally real' status to the con-cept of travelling when applied to light beams. The principle of essential connectivity, however, demands that in the lantern-mirror-screen system there be an additional difference to the differ-ence in the times of the departure and arrival of the light signals (which, for unexplained reasons, is regarded by Bridgman as a single difference). In order to comply with this demand we are forced to view the possible operation of interposing a screen on the path of the beam as a legitimate means to establish the reality of light in transit.

On reflection, one may detect a number of arbitrary elements in Bridgman's treatment of this subject. The important point, how-ever, is that it emphasizes again the basic difference between the concepts of causality and of connectivity. We may note that Bridg-man has never invoked the former. He presented us with two systems in which there was no problem whatever in explaining the differences between them in a causal sense. The fact that reflection occurred earlier in one system than in the other is explained causally by the fact that emission occurred earlier there. And why the emission occurred earlier in the first system is because the shutter of its lantern was lifted earlier. Nothing has happened that remains unexplained in the sense that it is undetermined or unpredictable.

Yet Bridgman thought there was still something essential lack-ing. The systems appeared to him to differ in one and only one disposition: they were disposed to differ in the times of luminosity

[1] P. W. Bridgman, *The Logic of Modern Physics* (Macmillan, 1954), p. 158.
[2] Ibid., p. 153.

at their terminal points. This trouble he remedies by declaring light in transit as real.

7. J. C. MAXWELL'S CRITERION FOR DISTINGUISHING BETWEEN REAL AND EMPTY PREDICATES

But what are the empirical foundations of the principle of connectivity? After all it is surely not a mere linguistic rule? This question cannot be answered as long as the concept of single property or single disposition remains shrouded in vagueness. The crucial point upon which depends the objective meaning of the demand for the association of different properties is the explication of the notion of isolated disposition.

Such explication would require a great deal of basic analysis. At the same time it would have far-reaching results leading to the clarification of many outstanding issues in the philosophy of science. One of these issues is 'physical realness'. The idea of physical realness is tightly coupled to the concept of connectivity and the next two sections will be devoted to discussing it. Let me begin by introducing from scratch the concepts of 'empty' and 'real' predicates.

About certain predicates we feel that they stand for real properties actually belonging to the physical entities predicated by them. About other predicates, though meaningful, as they have been defined in physically performable operations, we may feel they have been arbitrarily constructed and denote no real properties. The question arises whether there is any clear-cut rule as to how to distinguish those predicates that are thought to denote properties with real existence from contrived, empty predicates.

When a person has been, for example, subjected to an I.Q. test and his answers to the questions have been assessed in the standard manner, he is assigned a certain number. We suppose this number to represent the measure of the degree to which he possesses the property of intelligence. On the other hand, when recently a popular magazine invited its readers to answer questions from a questionnaire compiled to measure their 'intensity of character' all readers understood that the function of the test was to provide entertainment and not the means for measuring the value of any property human beings really possessed. Can we, however, give an articulate and completely general account of the precise circumstances under which the results obtained by a test through a questionnaire do or do not rate as representing the measure of some actual human characteristics?

Or again the pressure of a gas or the entropy of an aggregate are generally thought to denote real properties, whereas a term like W.I.Q.—capriciously defined as Weight × Intelligence Quotient —is not. Obviously the fact that W.I.Q. has been defined in terms of the result of a simple mathematical operation upon weight and I.Q., both variables representing real properties $\left(\text{just as pressure which}\right.$ is defined pressure $= \dfrac{\text{force}}{\text{area}}$ or entropy which is defined as entropy $= \displaystyle\int \left.\dfrac{\text{increase in heat}}{\text{temperature}}\right)$ is not capable of lending it substance. But here again the question arises whether we could lay down a general rule when to regard the result of a mathematical operation on physical parameters as representing a real physical property and when not.

The answer to our question does not appear too far to seek. Consider the predicate W.I.Q. Suppose we have made readings of the candidate's temperature throughout the whole of the duration of the I.Q. test and obtained the value of his average body temperature during that period. Suppose also that it was found, after performing such sets of operations at different times on our candidates and on other people, that W.I.Q. varied directly with average body temperature for every individual. It is quite obvious that, however unexpected such result may seem to us, we would change our attitude toward W.I.Q. and would no longer regard it as an empty word.

It is of course, not necessary that W.I.Q. should vary directly with body temperature. Once we succeed to show that W.I.Q. stands in some mathematical relationship to temperature or for that matter is a function of any other parameter associated with the human body, it will assume in our eyes the status of a real physical parameter. In fact, if W.I.Q. was not a function of any particular parameter but remained constant for the same individual person, this too would suffice for us not to dismiss it as vacuous.

In the same manner, if intensity of character were to be found, for example, varying in a definite fashion with the age of an individual or inheritable like other personal traits, or could be correlated with any other human characteristics or shown to be a mathematical function of any physical parameter of the human body, we would cease to think of it as an empty word.

All this amounts to saying that a predicate stands for a real property if a full description of it asserts something about reality by asserting an empirical law. When it is merely said that W.I.Q. = Weight × I.Q., then we have given an arbitrary definition. When, however, it is asserted that Weight × I.Q. = $f(p)$, where p is a property of human beings and f is some mathematical function, we are describing an empirical relationship. Thus the expression W.I.Q. = $f(p)$ which defines W.I.Q. embodies a 'real' aspect of the external world by virtue of which it may rate as being itself 'real'. Similarly when we describe intensity of character not merely in terms of the result obtained through an arbitrarily devised test but as something varying in a set fashion with, say, the age of the individual, we are asserting the existence of an empirical relationship.

What has been said so far is identical in essence with the ideas put forward on this issue by James Clerk Maxwell, although this may not be apparent on the first sight. Maxwell seems to be the first physicist who has voiced an explicit view on the question of these two types of predicates. In his terminology, he was trying to distinguish predicates which stand for 'physical states' from others which should be regarded as mere 'scientific concepts'. What he says is best understood from J. Turner's exposition of Maxwell's views [1] who summarizes them as asserting that a quantity, if it is connected to at least two independent physical phenomena, represents a physical state, otherwise it does not represent a physical state. He compares the predicates 'velocity' as applied to a given point in a fluid to 'electric force' (or 'field strength') as applied to a point in space and explains that whereas the former represents a 'physical state' of that particular point in the fluid, the latter is not to be regarded as an actual 'physical state' in which the point in question is.

The reason for the distinction is to be found in the fact that there is one and only one way to define the intensity of the electric force at a point; it is the force to which a unit charge would be subjected if placed at that point. The velocity of a fluid at a given point, on the other hand, can be defined in a number of independent ways. One

[1] J. Turner, 'Maxwell on Method of Physical Analogy', *British Journal for the Philosophy of Science*, 1955, Vol. VI, No. 23.

way, Turner says, would be to define it as the force which would act upon a small cork tied to a spring if placed at that point. Another way—assuming that the temperature of a fluid varied with its velocity—would be to define velocity in terms of the temperature at the given point.

Maxwell's demand that a concept be definable independently in two different ways before it may qualify to represent a physical state is not an arbitrary demand. His requirement amounts to the same as the stipulation that a predicate is vacuous unless its full description expresses an empirical law. When the velocity of a fluid at a certain point is defined both in terms of the behaviour of the cork tied to the spring and in terms of the temperature of the fluid we are asserting an empirical relationship, since the existence of a correlation between the two is an empirical law. When, however, we defined intensity of electric field as the force that would be experienced by a unit charge if placed there we have committed ourselves through our definition to no empirical relationship. The fact that this force varies with the distribution of charges upon the force-producing charged bodies, is already embodied in the description of charges and their behaviour which includes the statement that they act at distance in accordance with the inverse square law.

It should be also mentioned that the issues of these two types of predicates occupy a central role in the writings of P. W. Bridgman. Bridgman clearly adopts Maxwell's criterion when he declares that no physical reality should be ascribed to electric field for he

> ... cannot find a single physical phenomenon or a single physical operation by which evidence of the existence of the field may be obtained independent of the operations which entered the definition.[1]

He similarly echoes Maxwell when, considering the concept of 'stress' as applied to an elastic body, he announces that:

> ... we have a right to ascribe physical reality to it because it is uniquely connected with other physical phenomena *independent of those which entered its definition*.[2]

Throughout his writings Bridgman puts to Maxwell's test many predicates ranging from 'entropy' as applied to physical aggregates

[1] P. W. Bridgman, *The Logic of Modern Physics*, p. 59.
[2] Ibid., pp. 55–56.

to 'intelligence' as applied to human beings. He qualifies, however, Maxwell's approach in one respect, namely, by maintaining that the test need only be applied to attributes not directly disclosed to our senses. His standpoint seems reasonable that colour properties which manifest themselves directly to our eyes or temperature which we can feel may be regarded as real just for this reason alone. Yet Maxwell, who grants 'temperature' the status of a predicate which stands for a physical state, only does so because, as he points out in §66 of his 'Elementary Treatise on Electricity', a variation in temperature can be defined in terms of the variation in the magnitude of a number of physical properties such as density or conductivity.

It is characteristic of Bridgman to have scruples about the whole business of the 'reality' of concepts, an idea which makes them, as it were, transcend the operations in terms of which they were defined. To ease his operationist conscience he cautions that his:

> . . . requirements in fact, from the operational point of view amount to nothing more than a definition of what we mean by the reality of things not given directly by experience.[1]

Yet a few pages later he openly claims that we ought to treat predicates definable in more than one way differently from predicates not so definable, not on mere conventional grounds:

> This difference in the character of constructs may be expected to correspond to essential physical differences, and these physical differences are much too likely to be overlooked in the thinking of physicists.[2]

Before examining more thoroughly Maxwell's criterion of physical realness, it should be pointed out that he was the first only so far as the explicit formulation of the criterion is concerned, but the issue as such has occupied the minds of many scientists before him, who basically have adopted his attitude. To trace the whole history of the concept of the realness of predicates would take us too far afield but we shall consider one example.

For over two centuries scientists have applied themselves to the problem of *temperature intervals*. It was commonly agreed that thermometers employing different thermometric substances will

---

[1] P. W. Bridgman, *The Logic of Modern Physics*, p. 56.
[2] Ibid., p. 60.

reliably show when two bodies are at equal temperature and also, when they are not, which one is at a higher temperature. The temperature order of different bodies can uniquely be determined by any thermometer. Therefore the expressions 'equal temperatures', 'higher temperature' or 'lower temperature' were always regarded as representing physical states. It was, however, appreciated that when a thermometer has shown an increase of temperature from 0° to 20° it is in general senseless to claim that such an increase was twice as large as an increase from 0° to 10°. The degrees recorded on an ordinary thermometer were treated as rank order numbers determining the relative position of a body in the temperature series. The lengths of intervals on an arbitrary scale were not treated as though they were really proportional to actual lengths of temperature intervals. At the same time scientists firmly believed that eventually a 'rational scale' would be found, a scale which would truly reflect the magnitude of temperature.

Brook Taylor, in 1723, was one of those investigators who thought he had found such a scale. He adopted Newton's scale of temperature which employs linseed oil as the thermometric substance and on which melting ice was assigned zero temperature and boiling water twelve degrees of temperature. Taylor mixed eleven parts of freezing water with one part of boiling water and found that the temperature of the mixture was one degree on Newton's scale. He mixed freezing and boiling waters in a variety of proportions and always found that the temperature shown on Newton's scale was proportional to the quantity of boiling water in the mixtures. He concluded, therefore, that in Newton's scale he has found a rational scale of temperature.

Taylor's conclusion is based on the tacit adoption of Maxwell's criterion. He was prepared to treat as a real quantity that temperature interval which could be independently defined in terms of two operations—in terms of measurements by a linseed oil thermometer and in terms of the mixture method.

8. THE UNCERTAIN MEANING OF MAXWELL'S CRITERION

The close link between Maxwell's criterion of physical realness and the principle of connectivity is easily seen. Suppose that a given point in space is completely indistinguishable from some other point except for the fact that the intensity of electric field at the two points is different. This might seem to present a case in which the principle of connectivity was violated. By applying, however, Maxwell's criterion, we ensure that no such violation takes place. The intensity of field at a point in space is a mere scientific concept, it does not denote an actual property possessed by that point. Thus what seemed to be a single difference between the two points turns out to be not a *real* difference at all.

At the same time all the ambiguities encountered on analysing the notion of connectivity reappear when we analyse Maxwell's criterion. On what basis, we might ask, did both Maxwell and Bridgman claim that there is no more than one way to define the intensity of electric field? One could argue that there are a number of different ways. The force experienced by a unit charge, when placed at a point in the field, may be defined in terms of the acceleration of the test charge or alternatively in terms of the extension caused in the spring to which the test charge was attached. Then again, electric field strength could also be defined as half the force experienced by two unit charges. This definition is logically independent of the definition which says that field strength is the force experienced by one unit charge, for it is after all no more than an empirical fact that one unit charge experiences half the force experienced by two unit charges. Finally, we could define the intensity of an electric field altogether without the aid of test charges. We could arbitrarily specify what we shall regard as our standard unit field (e.g., the field produced by a conductor of such and such dimensions, etc., at such and such distance) and define the magnitude of any particular field as the number of unit electric fields required to counteract it.

If all these considerations are to be discounted then it is probably because the different operations we have suggested do after all measure forces and are consequently not deemed as independent of one another. The only way then in which the reality of the electric field could be established would be through a definition which would not refer to the concept of force at all. This seems to be Bridgman's opinion as explained by him in a later work:

> The situation might conceivably be improved if there were *two* or more independent instrumental means of verifying the existence of the field, such, for example, as the electrostatic double refraction which accompanies electrostatic field in transparent body. But apparently there are not two such independent instrumental

approaches in empty space, but the only instrumental meaning of the field is in terms of the force on test bodies.[1]

Thus we are told that operations measuring optical phenomena would rate as distinct from those measuring forces and a definition in terms of them may therefore be regarded as an independent alternative definition. It turns out, however, that even in this we cannot be quite certain, for in the very same paragraph Bridgman adds:

> But even if there were two or more independent means of demonstrating the existence of field, it is not at all obvious that we could then show that action at a distance is not an alternative method of description.

That is, since any observable property of the point in space can be explained in terms of the influence of distant charged bodies the concept of field can be dispensed with and may after all not qualify as physically real.

It is easily seen, that if these sort of considerations are admissible as well, then doubt can be cast upon the 'reality' of any concept. Bridgman was, for example, satisfied that one may ascribe physical reality to the 'stress' of an elastic body, because stress can be defined firstly as force per unit area upon the surface of the body and secondly as the product of rigidity modulus and strain. But here too the phenomena connected with elasticity lend themselves to an 'alternative method of description' in which, instead of making any reference to the extra concept 'stress', it is asserted that $\frac{force}{area}$ = rig. mod. $\times$ strain. Similarly Maxwell was satisfied that temperature, which varied with a great number of other physical parameters and hence could be defined alternatively in terms of these variations, represented a 'physical state'. But the concept of temperature too could be dispensed with and science, which would become more cumbersome as a result, could nevertheless get along by making use of the covariation of different parameters and without employing the correlating term, temperature. The only serious objection one could raise against the demotion of temperature would be from the fact that it makes itself directly felt to the senses and thus having a special claim for 'realness'.

[1] P. W. Bridgman, *The Nature of Some of Our Physical Concepts* (New York, 1956), p. 17.

It is then quite evident that properties which are not directly given by experience can never impose themselves upon the scientist without his consent. It is always up to him to decide whether or not to grant the status of a 'real property' to any candidate presenting itself for consideration. He may take advantage of the indeterminate nature of the concept of single disposition or declare a property non-real by deciding that it manifested itself in no more than one way. Conversely he may break up a seemingly single disposition into different ones. He may also shift a property from one ownership to another (as in the case of intensity of electric field at a point, which can be made to belong either to that given point or to the distant charged conductors). Furthermore it has become evident from a quick glance at the writings of those who have given the matter some thought, that there are no agreed rules by which we may foretell the attitude scientists will take in any particular instance.

9. CONCLUSION

From our survey it has become evident that neither the principle that 'two substances never differ in one property alone' nor the principle that 'differences in the behaviour of systems do not occur isolated but are associated with other differences' are definite assertions about the nature of the physical world. For no objective criterion has been laid down as to what is to be regarded as an isolated behaviour, a single property or a single disposition. The principle of connectivity as a statement about the universe is indeterminate. It should, however, be emphasized that it is far from being therefore devoid of all significance.

The sentiments expressed by these authors are, after all, universally shared. We all feel that not only events or changes need to be correlated to other events or changes. If two systems appear to us to differ in having one dissimilar disposition, we think of the situation as an anomalous one. It will not suffice to have 'explained' how that single disposition came into being (by correlating its rise with some other change in the universe). It does not seem enough to 'account' for physical dispositions in terms of the past. When faced with an ostensibly single disposition we insist that *at present* there resides in the very same system some other *co-existing* disposition. We shall not be satisfied until this additional disposition is not produced either by verbal manipulation or by empirical discovery.

The principle may therefore meaningfully be stated as an assertion about an ingrained form of thought or about a conceptual necessity. It may be said that 'there exists a universal tendency not to allow systems to differ—in what appears to the mind a single disposition'. This assertion has implications in the realms of: the expectations of scientists; scientific language and also the empirical results of science.

If we regard two physical systems as tested in every way—except with respect to one disposition—and as found perfectly identical, we expect them to be identical with respect to the yet untested (and what appears to us an 'isolated') disposition. If our expectations are not fulfilled we may remedy the trouble by verbal means. But we may also endeavour and consequently succeed, to discover empirically some additional differences between the two systems.

Science abounds in evidence of the impact made upon its course by the universal quest for connections other than the prediction ensuring causal ones. Consider, for example, the well known series of attempts made in the 17th century to 'explain' the colour differences of light rays. Why did Descartes feel obliged to come forward with the suggestion that the colour of light rays depends on the relative rapidity of the rotary motion and the linear motion of the small particles of which light consists; or Hooke with the suggestion that colour depends on whether the weaker or the stronger part was at the front or at the back of a light pulse? What urged scientists to produce these fanciful explanations? Surely they did not provide us with anything from which colour differences could in any way—logically or on the basis of some familiar model—be derived. Neither did they facilitate the prediction of colour phenomena which are just as predictable without it. For without knowing anything about the structure of light rays themselves we can know by experience which chemical compounds emit blue and which emit red light when incandescent and what substances transmit/reflect/absorb what light rays.

But the reason for all these endeavours to explain colour differences was that it was felt to be insufficient merely to find dissimilarities in the sources of emission, the substances traversed or the reflecting surfaces. Additional differences had to be found attributable to the differently coloured light rays themselves. In spite of the fact that colour phenomena did in no way violate the physicists' conception of order and causality in nature it still remained incomprehensible. For it was unthinkable that when two light rays differ in colour this difference should manifest itself in no other way but the way it affects the eye.

One is naturally tempted to exclaim here: but surely it would be a conceptual absurdity if two perfectly identical light rays should give rise to different experiences. It is, after all, by the famous dictum 'same cause, same effect', a dictum to which we all subscribe, that identical physical stimuli are expected to cause identical sense perceptions.

It may be hoped, however, that the reader who has followed the foregoing discussion will, upon reflection, realize that it is not on the basis of the above dictum that we demand a difference in the structure of the two light rays. For the light rays are anyhow not perfectly identical. They differ from each other by the very fact that they always and in everybody produce different colour experiences. This difference is conjoined by the fact that they hail from different sources and is therefore a predictable difference. It is by virtue of the principle of connectivity that we are yet not satisfied and find the situation still conceptually anomalous.

The relevance of Newton's work, to this problem of associating colour properties with some other properties of light rays themselves, is noteworthy. It is with him that differences in the disposition of light rays to produce different colour perception were correlated with another *observable* difference in their dispositions, namely: different refrangibility. Newton has shown that as we move along the spectrum of colours from red to violet each successive colour is slightly more refrangible than the one before. Thus, apart from all the practical consequences of Newton's discovery, it was an important turning point in the history of optics; colour phenomena ceased to be anomalous and became fully comprehensible.

4

THE PRINCIPLE
OF VERIFICATION

I. INTRODUCTION

THE subjects of this essay have so far been dealt with in the order of decreasing familiarity. But the theme of this final chapter would seem to be a rather well-known one. In fact it caused more controversy and discussion for several decades in the present century than any other topic in philosophy.

It is, however, sometimes easier to put forward an entirely new idea than to advance convincingly a considerably modified version of an established one. I shall endeavour to present the principle of verification in a different light from that in which it is commonly viewed. The advantage of having postponed its treatment to this stage will soon emerge. It is important to have had some picture of the rather elusive character of the principles of methodology; to have seen how they pendulate between the vagueness of tentative maxims and the concreteness of productive rules, exhibiting at once both elements of empirical and verbal truth, before one can assign the proper place of this principle among the other principles of methodology.

The principle of verification as commonly interpreted both by adherents and opponents would at first appear altogether out of place in this essay. Methodological rules are understood to be rules governing the techniques of working scientists. They are not a part of the superstructure, but of science itself. They are employed not in interpreting the results of science but in producing them.

The principle of verification seems to belong to an entirely different category. It is a rule prescribing the circumstances under which propositions and concepts[1] become meaningful. The meanings of terms representing concepts, and of sentences which express theories and laws, may be of interest to philosophers who seek understanding for the sake of understanding, but not for practical scientists striving to acquire an understanding that may enable them to anticipate and influence the course of nature.

The principle of verification is not thought of as a principle within the framework of science but rather as a structural part of that framework itself. It governs the rules of the language of scientific discourse as well as everyday discourse. The investigation of 'meanings' whether by using the verificationist criterion or any other criterion is expected to lead to a feeling of enlightenment and of deeper insight but not to any concrete results in science.

The feelings of the practical scientist toward philosophical discussions on the meanings of concepts and propositions are often those expressed by Professor Lazerowitz's quip, 'the child sees that the emperor is naked but philosophers instead argue over whether a man who wears an invisible robe is dressed.'

Here, however, I shall endeavour to exhibit a different facet of the notion of 'meaning', one which will bring it into the orbit of our inquiries conducted throughout this essay. True enough, causal bystanders, insensitive to the finer aspects of metaphysics, overhearing the philosophers arguing among themselves whether the emperor is to be regarded as dressed or naked, may feel indifferent about the final outcome of this debate. They may feel completely unmoved upon learning that these philosophers have ultimately agreed to adopt a criterion of meaning whereby wearing an

---

[1] Concepts themselves are not amenable to verification for they are neither true nor false. They are often therefore said to become meaningful by a different principle, that of operationalism (e.g. by Carl G. Hempel in *The Validation of Scientific Theories*, Boston, p. 52). This states: A concept is meaningful if the operations in terms of which it is defined can be given. It is not necessary however to think of two different principles of meaning. The verification principle can apply to concepts as well: A concept is meaningful if statements in which it is used can be verified.

There is no fundamental difference between Logical Positivism, Logical Empiricism or Verificationism on the one hand and Operationism on the other. It is only that while the former usually concentrate upon meaning in ordinary discourse the latter discusses meaning in scientific discourse.

invisible robe means something fundamentally different from being naked. But when eventually this linguistic distinction seems to manifest itself in a concrete fashion, as for instance when later upon the weather's turning chilly all lightly dressed people shiver with cold while the emperor continues to proceed unperturbed, then the philosophers' criterion becomes a matter of interest to more practically minded people too.

This parable—for the want of a better one—is intended to indicate what I should like to show to be the case with regard to the philosophical topic at hand. Although verificational analysis and the principle of meaning based on it are subjects mainly discussed by philosophers they can also be exhibited as the source of concrete results in science—provided they are correctly understood. That the principle of verification which is normally understood to be a principle of meaning should also feature as a methodological principle need not surprise us. Indeed the reason for it doing so will appear a most natural one if we are prepared to accept the view that the verificationist method of analysis did not come into being by arbitrary stipulation, that in fact its shaping has been influenced by certain outstanding features of the methodological techniques employed successfully by scientists in their investigations.

This last point is by no means an original one. In fact it is the central idea underlying P. W. Bridgman's Operationism, expressed by him explicitly on numerous occasions, as in the concluding sentence of one of his more recent articles:

> It must be remembered that the operational point of view suggested itself from the observations of physicists in action.[1]

Nor is the idea of the blending of a methodological rule into a rule determining the meanings of scientific discourse introduced here for the first time into this essay. The present case is not altogether unlike what we have already found to be the case in our investigations of the principle of connectivity. Once it has come to our attention that two systems are not identical with one another, the principle bids us to search for further dissimilarities. It is then basically a methodological rule. At the same time, as we have seen, the principle functions as a rule of language, for instance in determining what we shall call a 'different' aspect and what we shall call the 'same' aspect.

[1] *The Validation of Scientific Theories* (Boston, 1957), p. 79.

My main concern in this chapter will be to emphasize the practical side of the verification principle and to exhibit it as a methodological principle comparable in status to the principles dealt with previously. I shall try to show how the principle is employed by physicists while engaged in the activity of scientific research and not only when philosophizing about it.

An indispensable prerequisite for this is the introduction of a most important idea, the idea of *comparative meaning*. What both friendly and hostile commentators of verificationism and operationism as a rule concentrate upon is the problem which propositions or concepts are meaningful and which are meaningless. The outcome of such an investigation, however, is of not much consequence to the working scientist. It is the study of comparative meaning which leads to practical results. It will be necessary to explain very carefully what precisely I mean by 'comparative meaning', for on the whole hardly any explicit reference is ever made to it.

In these preliminary remarks it will suffice if I give the following brief explanation: The scope of operational or verificational analysis of meaning is not merely restricted to the investigation of whether concepts or propositions are meaningful or meaningless. It is also possible, and this seems to be of far greater interest, to employ operational or verificational analysis to distinguish between the meanings of various propositions and concepts. When we analyse a certain proposition P_1 not with the aim of discovering whether it has meaning at all or is completely devoid of it, but whether it has the same meaning or a different meaning as proposition P_2, then we will be said to be studying the comparative meaning of P_1 and P_2.

2. THE TECHNICAL–PHYSICAL–LOGICAL TRICHOTOMY

The verification principle which was put forward by its originators in the earnest conviction that it would provide a panacea for all the ills of philosophy, has right from the beginning become the target of vigorous attacks. In the process of the lively and intensive discussions which were provoked, fundamental difficulties in the original conception of the principle were soon made evident. Nowadays, indeed, on reading some of the early literature of verificationism, one is often wondering how it was possible so comparatively recently for philosophers to adopt such untenable positions. It is also evident that in spite of the successive painstaking efforts of Logical Positivists to reformulate their principle and state modified versions of it, they have not quite succeeded in mending the breaches in its foundations.

This section will be devoted to an illustration of one of the perplexing questions that has arisen in connection with the principle: how do we interpret the term 'possibility of verification' or 'verifiable in principle'? The elaboration of this point is in no way a digression from our main topic—comparative meaning. For later it will be seen that this problem, however ineradicable, does not at all affect the significance of an analysis made in order to determine comparative meaning. 'Verifiability in principle' does not come into such analysis. In fact most of the criticism directed against verificationism is irrelevant to it as far as its comparative function is concerned. It is absolute verificationism according to which one can and should classify all utterances into meaningful discourse and nonsensical verbiage, which lays itself open to all sorts of attack. This ought to provide us with additional incentive to inquire into the nature and scope of comparative meaning.

Let us, then, see what difficulties the concept of 'verifiability in principles' raises. It has generally been assumed by all verificationists and explicitly asserted by many, that the drawing of a clear demarcation line between the different types of the concept of 'possibility' is an indispensable prerequisite for any investigation of meaning. When we have acquired the means to identify the different concepts of possibility, it is supposed that the next thing to do is to decide on the type of possibility that will serve as our criterion against which to test the meaningfulness of human discourse. Then, and only then, can we embark upon the analysis of the significance of individual propositions and concepts.

For, as M. Schlick explains, when we say that 'a proposition has meaning only if it is verifiable' we are not saying 'if it is *verified*'. Verifiability means the possibility of verification. But often a proposition not actually verifiable could nevertheless be verified in principle, because an operation that is needed for the confirmation of a proposition may be impossible to perform in one sense (say, technically) yet possible to perform in another sense (physically). Therefore the question arises what type of possibility do we choose as our criterion of meaning. On this choice will depend, in the case of many propositions, whether they have or have not any meaning.

In general the existence of three types of possibilities is recognized. Something said to be impossible may be either logically or empirically or technically impossible. Feigl[1] and Reichenbach,[2] for instance, both agree that the choice between these three is largely an arbitrary affair. But, as Reichenbach explains, if we regard even operations which are merely technically unperformable as inadmissible, our theory of meaning will be too narrow, excluding much that is valuable for science. On the other hand if we regard as inadmissible only operations that are logically impossible, our theory of meaning becomes too wide, excluding hardly anything. Therefore they suggest physical possibility as the criterion of meaning. An operation physically performable, even though not technically performable, is qualified to lend meaning to concepts and propositions.

If this criterion is to be effective then one must be able to distinguish clearly between what is physically and what is merely technically impossible. The authors do not explicate the distinction in general terms but produce examples to illustrate it. These examples suggest that technical impossibility is an impossibility that stems from our ignorance and is therefore likely to be a temporary one, whereas physical impossibility is a permanent impossibility rooted in nature itself. Thus, for example, Feigl censures August Comte for having committed 'a typical reductive fallacy' by pronouncing the question of the chemical constitution of stars a meaningless one, just because in his time there was no known procedure for answering that question.[3] But Feigl does not indicate by what method Comte should have arrived at the conclusion that the solution to the problem of the constitution of the stars was bound up with mere technical-practical difficulties but not with physical ones. It is altogether questionable whether one could ever claim with certainty about something one is unable to do, that in principle it could be done. It seems that not until a practical problem is solved do we know for sure that there is nothing inherent in nature to prevent its solution.

[1] H. Feigl & W. Sellars, *Readings in Philosophical Analysis* (New York, 1949), p. 502.

[2] H. Reichenbach, *Experience and Prediction* (Chicago, 1938), p. 41.

[3] *Readings in Philosophical Analysis*, p. 10.

Strictly speaking then, the label 'technically impossible' can be attached only to something in retrospect, after it has ceased to be a technical impossibility. Only when one becomes capable of carrying out an operation does it become evident that previously there were no fundamental obstacles to its being carried out.

But this difficulty is not necessarily unsurmountable. It may yet be possible to devise a definition of the technical-physical dichotomy, a definition which may be clear and comprehensive enough to be applied without much ambiguity to most cases. One possible approach might be to stipulate that an act which cannot be performed but which is not positively ruled out by any known law of current theory is to be regarded as a technically unperformable act. If, however, the carrying out of an operation would definitely involve the violation of some known physical law then that operation is to be regarded as physically impossible. A weekend trip to Mars and a weekend trip to Betelgeuse would then represent technical and physical impossibilities respectively. For whereas neither can actually be undertaken at present, against the feasibility of the latter one may cite the law that nothing can travel faster than light and this, together with the fact that Betelgeuse is many light years away, makes it a physical impossibility. Thus if we could suggest no other method for the solution of a problem except one which would require such a journey, that problem would have to be regarded as meaningless.

On reflection one can easily see that not all is well with this definition either, but I do not propose to pursue the point any farther. There is a far more decisive objection to the construction of a theory of meaning based on 'physically possible verification'. If this criterion is to be adopted, then, as Reichenbach explains, the statements that the temperature of the interior of the sun is forty million degrees of heat becomes meaningless, since the physicist and his instrument would burn up long before they came near the sun to carry out temperature measurements. But a theory of meaning of this kind has no bearing whatsoever on the one to which scientists subscribe. As we know scientists do talk about happenings in the interior of the sun; they do talk about the interior of the atomic nuclei which are more inaccessible, and will not even refrain from talking about the interior of the nucleus of an atom in the interior of the sun.

Let us examine then the alternative suggestion that as soon as an operation is logically possible it qualifies for lending meaning to concepts and propositions. M. Schlick is the representative of this view and in his opinion logical possibility is the only feasible criterion to be adopted. A proposition is devoid of meaning if, and only if, for its verification an appeal would have to be made to operations which are logically unperformable. A statement about the temperature of the interior of the sun is meaningful as it is logically conceivable that the physicist and his instrument should penetrate unscorched into the innermost parts of the sun. But what propositions do become meaningless by this criterion? Examples are provided by Schlick himself:

> Take some examples. The sentence, 'My friend died the day after tomorrow'; 'The lady wore a dark red dress which was bright green'; 'The campanile is 100 feet and 150 feet high'; 'The child was naked but wore a long nightgown', obviously violate the rules which in ordinary English govern the use of words occurring in the sentences. They do not describe any facts at all; they are meaning-less, because they represent logical impossibilities.[1]

The immediate impression gained upon reading these examples is that a theory of meaning based on the criterion of logical possibility is a trivial one. It excludes nothing we could not have excluded without it. With the aid of such theory we are not going to detect and remove from science something of consequence that has escaped our notice and was responsible for giving rise to wrong theories.

In order to meet this objection, of course, one could point out that not all contradictions are as obvious as those quoted by Schlick. In cases of many highly complex propositions, as we know, it may require the use of elaborate techniques to detect a contradiction. The important point, however, is that even if self-contradictory statements can only sometimes be exposed with the aid of highly skilled logical or mathematical operations, once they are exposed they will be rejected by all scientists irrespective of verificationism. No matter how philosophers may feel about self-contradictory propositions, regardless of the fact that there are some who claim they are meaningful,[2] practical scientists have never had any use for them. By declaring such propositions as meaningless one feels noth-ing has been achieved as far as science is concerned.

[1] *Readings in Philosophical Analysis*, p. 154.
[2] M. Lazerowitz, *The Structure of Metaphysics*, pp. 231–253.

Before finally concluding that logical possibility cannot serve as our criterion for meaningfulness if verification is to be of any significance, we may note that Schlick's examples could be claimed to be irrelevant to the idea they were supposed to illustrate. If the category of logical impossibility is to be parallel to the categories of physical and technical impossibilities, then the proper examples are not those propositions which themselves constitute a self-contradiction, but those for whose verification one has to appeal to logically impossible operations. Indeed Reichenbach, when proposing the three types of possibilities, says explicitly:

> It must be kept in mind that these three concepts of possibility are to be applied to the method of verification and not to the fact described by the proposition.[1]

A moment's reflection will convince us that no proposition exists which in itself is not self-contradictory but the verification of which is logically impossible. The simple reason being that as we are neither tied to any particular means of verification nor bound by the laws of the empirical world which we may suppose violated, there is always an infinite number of ways to stipulate means of verification not violating the laws of logic.

True enough, a particular method of verification may sometimes be logically precluded. The proposition that 'the whole universe, every single object contained in it, started to increase in size at a certain rate this morning' may perhaps be claimed to be logically unverifiable by that particular method in which a yardstick is used —in the manner in which yardsticks are used—to measure the increase of other objects. For the assumption that such an operation may lead to the confirmation of our proposition contradicts what has been stated in it. We have explicitly stated that everything has increased in size since this morning—this includes our yardstick too. Claiming to be able to measure an increase in length by a yardstick presupposes that the yardstick itself has not changed in length —hence the contradiction.

But there can certainly be no objection on purely logical grounds to our stipulating that the temperature, conductivity, specific heat, electric resistance and magnetic permeability are a unique function of the length of every object. Calculating the co-variance of these parameters will verify our statement.

[1] H. Reichenbach, *Experience and Prediction*, p. 39.

3. WEAK VERIFICATION

At the moment it would seem that not only is it incorrect to claim that there are three categories of 'possibilities' from which we are at liberty to choose the criterion of meaningfulness, but that we are left with not even one category upon which to base a theory of meaning useful to science. For as we have seen, if every proposition which was physically impossible to verify had to be discarded, then much which no scientist would be prepared to reject would have to be declared nonsense. Needless to say that to insist on the technical possibility of the verification of propositions would be even more absurd. On the other hand, if logical possibility was all that we required, our criterion would be ineffective in cleansing science from any undesirable element.

The way out of this difficulty has been found through the realization that there are different grades of verification and that one need not insist on the direct and perfect verifiability of meaningful statements. It has been appreciated that the great majority of statements which are regarded as well-grounded scientific statements are neither completely verified nor completely verifiable, but are corroborated or supported by observation to different degrees. Consequently, recently verificationists have required no more than the physical possibility of the testing of a proposition, which, however, need not amount to conclusive evidence but to 'weak verification' or 'partial confirmation'. They are now satisfied if the facts lend support to a given statement, no matter in how indirect or weak fashion. A proposition may be regarded as meaningful if, together with other empirically valid theories and hypotheses, it entails some observation statement.

Reichenbach, for example, who finally comes round to subscribing to this point of view, concludes that it is after all meaningful to assign a value for the temperature of the interior of the sun and that this would ultimately rest upon actual observations. Assuming a value for the temperature gradient along the radius of the sun which we derive from a conjunction of theories and observations and assuming the validity of the laws of radiation, the assertion about the internal temperature of the sun entails a certain statement about the reading recorded on an instrument which measures the amount of energy contained in the light rays received from the sun. Thus the statement about the temperature at the centre of the sun is finally grounded in empirical facts. These facts are the recordings of the energy measuring graduated instrument and the facts upon which our theories of radiation and temperature gradient rest.

Bridgman adopts a very similar attitude when he demands that every meaningful scientific term must permit of an operational definition, and at the same time concedes that such an operation may be only a 'paper and pencil' operation and need only ultimately be connected to actual instrumental operations. He says:

> It will be seen that a very great latitude is allowed to the verbal and the paper and pencil operations. I think however that physicists are agreed in imposing one restriction on the freedom of such operations, namely that such operations must be capable of eventually, although perhaps indirectly making connection with instrumental operation.[1]

It is needless to enter into detailed analysis in order to show that this revised and weakened principle is not as yet philosophically satisfactory either. For one thing it is too vague. It has not specified how indirect the connection between a proposed statement and instrumental operations may be, or how those theories and hypotheses, with the aid of which the proposed statement may lead to observation statements, have themselves qualified as empirically true.

These difficulties and others have been noted by verificationists and various attempts to tighten up the principle have already been made. We may for our purposes assume that these attempts have led or will eventually lead to complete success and that all the objections to the principle will be eliminated. Be it as it may, by now it should be perfectly clear that this kind of principle is very different from the one we were discussing in the first section of this chapter. The modified principle as outlined here cannot be counted as a principle among other principles within science. It is rather a definition of the essence of science itself or at any rate of what science has meant for the last three hundred years at least. No scientist will ever want to include within physical theory a concept or a hypothesis which has no bearing whatsoever on the empirical world.

The modified verification principle as it appears now underlies the whole of science and could therefore not be regarded as a methodological principle. No specific result can possibly be claimed

---

[1] *The Nature of Some of our Physical Concepts* (New York 1956), p. 10.

to have been achieved through the application of the principle. This is of crucial importance from our point of view. For it has been precisely for the alleged ability of the principle to weed out meaningless concepts and hypotheses that have taken root in science, that philosophically minded scientists have hailed it as a fundamental methodological principle. The most spectacular result ordinarily attributed to the application of the principle is the Special Theory of Relativity. We could therefore do no better than to examine the way the concept of absolute simultaneity has been rejected and see that no basis for this rejection can be found in the principle as it is commonly interpreted and has so far been described.

The idea that the verification principle has played a role in the abandonment of absolute simultaneity as a meaningless notion goes back to Einstein himself. The relevant passage occurs in his discussion of the simultaneity of two lightning strokes:

> ... We thus require a definition of simultaneity such that this definition supplies us with the means by which, in the present case, he can decide by experiment whether both lightning strokes occurred simultaneously. As long as this requirement is not satisfied, I allow myself to be deceived as a physicist (and of course the same applies if I am not a physicist) when I imagine that I am able to attach a meaning to the statement of simultaneity.[1]

This point has been reiterated with greater emphasis by various other scientists, as, for example, by Sir C. G. Darwin:

> The general point of view of questioning the reality of anything unobservable is one of the greatest revolutions in scientific thought that has ever occurred.[2]
> The great idea which Einstein contributed to scientific philosophy was the principle that if a thing is essentially unobservable then it is not a real thing and our theories must not include it.[3]

Philipp Frank in his contribution to the volume *Albert Einstein: Philosopher–Scientist*[4] claims that the impetus to the rise of the philosophical movement known as Logical Positivism, of which the verification principle forms the basic tenet, came from Ein-

---

[1] A. Einstein, *The Theory of Relativity* (1920), p. 22.
[2] C. G. Darwin, *The New Conception of Matter* (1931), p. 23.
[3] Ibid., p. 81.
[4] *The Library of Living Philosophers*, Vol. VII (ed. P. A. Schilpp, 1949).

stein's methodology. H. Dingle in the same volume argues that scientists before Einstein did not realize their fault in granting admission to concepts like absolute motion, length and simultaneity which are not 'referable to experience' and that it was Einstein who has pointed out the meaninglessness of such notions.

Bridgman, too, sees in Einstein's work the foundation of Operationism. Before Einstein—he explains—it was taken for granted that simultaneity was an intrinsic property of events themselves. It was not appreciated that the statement 'these two events occurred simultaneously' does not assume any meaning before one has carefully examined in exactly what way (e.g., how to set up our clocks; how to send light signals; how to measure distances and velocities, etc.) this statement is to be confirmed.

> Out of the examination of what we do in comparing the clocks we all know came Einstein's revolutionary recognition that the property of two events which hitherto had been unthinkingly called simultaneity involves in the doing a complicated sequence of physical operations which cannot be uniquely specified unless we specify who it is that is reading the clocks. We know that a consequence of this is that different observers do not always get the same result, so that simultaneity is not an absolute property of two events, but is relative to the observing system, that is, the system that does the things that constitute the measurement. What Einstein was in effect doing in this instance was to inquire into the meaning of simultaneity, and he was finding the meaning by analysing the physical operations employed in applying the concept in any concrete instance.[1]

Bridgman emphasizes elsewhere that what Einstein has shown was that the concept of absolute time is *meaningless*. It would be a mistake to think that he has shown 'something new about nature', namely, that absolute time which was thought to exist *did not in fact exist* but that he was:

> . . . merely bringing to light implications already contained in the physical operations used in measuring time.[2]

and:

> Therefore the previous statement that absolute time does not exist is replaced by the statement that absolute time is meaningless.[2]

[1] *Nature of Physical Theory*, p. 8.
[2] *Logic of Modern Physics*, p. 6.

And indeed, had we adopted earlier the operational theory of meaning then:

> . . . it should not have needed the new experimental facts which led to relativity to convince us of the inadequacy of our previous concepts, but that a sufficiently shrewd analysis should have prepared us for at least the possibility of what Einstein did.[1]

The new 'experimental facts' mentioned in the last paragraph refer, of course, to the Michelson–Morley experiment which resulted in the failure to measure our velocity relative to the aether. Before that, it was thought that the velocity of the Earth relative to the aether could uniquely be determined. It should be emphasized therefore that if, prior to this experiment, scientists would have been challenged to make explicit the operations upon which their concept of the absolute simultaneity of distant events rested, they could have easily done so. On the assumption of the measurability of the velocities of bodies relative to the aether, any event can be assigned a unique position on an absolute time scale. One needs only to ascertain the distance between the observer and the point at which a particular event took place and time the arrival of the light signal indicating the occurrence of the event. True enough, when the details of all the hypotheses and measurements involved have been enumerated, one comes to realize that the absolute simultaneity of remote events could not have been defined as directly in terms of physical operations as could the simultaneity of local events. But it has already been agreed that verificationism does not insist upon the immediate connection between our concepts and operations. In fact, the concept of absolute simultaneity of distant events would still stand in a more direct relationship to instrumental operations than many a respectable and common physical concept. There is no justification, therefore, for claiming that sound operational analysis alone should have revealed the inadequacy of the old concept of simultaneity.

Even after the shift in the attitude of the scientists when they have accepted the view that the velocity of light is the same in all directions, the indirect definition of the concept of absolute simultaneity in terms of instrumental operations has not become a physical impossibility. One might have attempted, for example, to define the absolute simultaneity of distant events in terms of the identical

[1] *Logic of Modern Physics*, p. 1.

time readings on two clocks which have been synchronized when close together and one of which has consequently been moved to the distant place. Whether such an attempt will lead to success, i.e., whether the clocks will remain synchronized no matter where, how and with what velocity one of them is moved, cannot be established on the basis of pure conceptual analysis alone.

The crucial point, which I believe can be brought out without entering into any further technical details of relativity theory, is the following: Einstein advanced the hypothesis that there is no absolute time scale, but that time scales differ for observers moving with different velocities. To this assumption he applied powerful mathematics and he has demonstrated that in conjunction with a number of other assumptions his hypothesis of relative time scales entails certain far-reaching observational results. As we know, these predictions have one after the other been confirmed. Had these predictions turned out to be false this would have been taken (provided that no new plausible hypotheses were introduced to explain away the failure of these predictions) as an indirect falsification of Einstein's hypothesis, and at the same time as an indirect verification that the alternative classical hypothesis was true. Things being as they are the converse is now the case. At any rate, the proposition that absolute time does not exist is either true or false, for it lends itself to indirect verification. The phenomenal success of Einstein's predictions demonstrate not that the hypothesis of an absolute time scale is *meaningless* but that it is likely to be *false* and the alternative assumption of a relative time scale is *true*.

It could still, of course, be correct to claim that if absolute time does not exist, then within certain time–space intervals it is meaningless to talk about a particular event having occurred before, after, or simultaneously with another particular event. This, however, would be the same type of meaningless talk as the famous inquiry whether the King of France is or is not bald when there is no King of France. In other words, we shall be prepared to admit that propositions presupposing false propositions are meaningless. But this will not help to establish the special significance of the principle of verification.

For the situation with regards to this type of meaningless talk is the same as the one we have already discussed in the previous section regarding the meaninglessness of self-contradictory propositions. Verificationists may want to insist that it is meaningless to talk about the baldness of the King of France *because* this cannot be verified as there is no King of France. To the practical scientist this contention, however, is a trivial one. It does not matter why such a proposition is to be regarded as devoid of meaning, or indeed whether it is to be regarded as devoid of meaning. It is taken for granted that propositions presupposing false propositions should not be entertained. Had 19th-century scientists been prepared to accept the idea that absolute time did not exist, they could have realized—without necessarily having to adopt a new philosophical outlook—that one is to refrain from talking about the simultaneity of distant events without first giving a definition of 'simultaneous'.

Thus, by maintaining the diluted version of verification and demanding that a concept must ultimately make reference to some instrumental operation, or asserting that unless a proposition has a bearing on actual experience the concept or proposition is devoid of empirical significance, one does not of necessity arrive at the Special Theory of Relativity. There is no basis for seeing in the theory the fruits of the application of the verification principle. Similarly there will be found no basis for seeing in any other concrete result of science the outcome of the application of the revised principle of verification.

True enough, as has already been suggested in the first chapter, the banishment of the caloric fluid from science, after it has been stripped of all practical significance, or the rejection of the crystalline spheres which have for centuries been carrying the planets along their orbits but which by the middle of the 17th century have become entirely redundant and in no way even remotely connected with anything tangible, may be regarded as deriving from the verification principle. But to claim that the rejection of any theory and its replacement by another through which concrete results are anticipated derives from the indirect, weak principle of verification, would be a contradiction in terms.

This by no means detracts from the philosophical importance of efforts like those of Carnap[1] to explicate in precise terms the nature of weak verificationism. But these efforts, like all efforts to make explicit the fundamental principles underlying empirical reasoning, will, if they succeed, give us a comprehensive exposition of the

[1] In his *The Methodological Character of Theoretical Concepts, Minnesota Studies in the Philosophy of Science*, Vol. 1.

nature of scientific thought and not of a methodological rule within science.

So far, then, it has not become evident how the verification principle could be counted among the methodological principles that have formed the object of our study.

4. THE COMPARATIVE FUNCTION OF ANALYSIS: THE DIFFERENTIAL ASPECT

The reason why it now seems untenable to regard verificationism as a methodological rule within science is that we have concentrated only on one aspect of verificationism. We have assumed—what is assumed practically by everyone else—that the sole function of verificational or operational analysis is to separate the meaningful from the meaningless. With its aid we expect to detect meaningless elements that have infiltrated into science, philosophy and everyday discourse, expose them and eliminate them. The more productive function of such analysis, namely to distinguish between meaningful propositions and concepts themselves, is hardly if ever mentioned.

It ought to be clear, however, that inquiry need not be confined to the mere investigation whether a concept is at all meaningful. Analysis need not stop as soon as the meaningfulness of a concept has been established, as it is of further interest to us what particular meaning it possesses. For there are different sorts of meanings and operationism teaches that these depend on the kinds of operations to which a concept is susceptible. By discovering these differences we may anticipate hitherto unsuspected practical differences. Through operational analysis we may predict or explain experimental results which would otherwise be difficult to account for.

Let me give a detailed example of a striking use of this type of analysis. It is taken from the writings of Bridgman. Let me just remark that even though we may find numerous examples in Bridgman's writings of the use of operational analysis in order to investigate comparative meaning, when it comes to an exposition of the aim and scope of operationism in general terms, he himself makes no explicit reference to it. But there are plenty of examples which speak clearly for themselves and his suggested solution to the well-known Gibb's Paradox in thermodynamics is one of them.

Gibb's paradox concerns a limiting process which, while from the physical point of view appears to be continuous, is represented mathematically as an abruptly discontinuous process. The paradox arose through his studying the phenomenon of the diffusion of gases.

When two volumes of gases diffuse into one another a change in entropy takes place. The total value of the entropy of the mixture is larger than the total value of entropy associated with the volumes when separated. This increase is called the 'entropy of mixture'. It is of a given magnitude which is independent of the nature of the gases involved. There is one exception, namely, when the two volumes consists of identical gases. In this case the entropy of mixture is zero. It clearly must be so, as the parts of a uniform gas keep inter-diffusing into each other all the time and evidently no endless increase of entropy results from this.

Now let us imagine a series of instances in which two volumes of gases are allowed to diffuse into one another. Let each instance differ from the one preceding it in that the gases involved are slightly more similar to one another, until in the last instance they are completely identical.

Gibb's paradox is this: Physically this limiting process is a continuous one. However, the value of entropy of mixture assigned by our theory is the same in each instance except in the last one when it abruptly drops to zero.

Against this, Bridgman argues that the paradox arose from a lack of appreciation that physically, too, there occurred an abrupt change in the process of limitation. This will be realized as soon as we adopt the 'operationist' attitude and analyse the meaning of the term 'different' gases. The meaning, of course, depends on the operation by which two 'different' gases can be distinguished:

It is assumed that this operation can still be performed and has meaning during all stages of the limiting process, as the two gases are allowed to become more similar. Of course this condition becomes more and more difficult to realize instrumentally, but verbally the formulation remains the same. But in the final step of the limiting process there is an abrupt discontinuity in the instrumental process: the two gases now become 'identical', which means that there is no instrumental operation performable now by which they may be distinguished, but the instrumental operations by which two molecules are to be distinguished would demand a determination of the history of each molecule, according as it was originally in the right-hand side of the box. Such operations are only pencil and paper operations, not the laboratory operations on which thermodynamics is predicated and which give entropy its meaning. Since the universe of operations of the limit differs discontinuously from that of the preceding stages, the argument for the continuity of any function such as entropy fails.[1]

The first thing we may notice is that in the whole argument no use is made of the notion of 'meaningless'. The concept of self-diffusion may be meaningful—what matters, however, is that it differs essentially from the concept of the diffusion of one gas into another.

Next, if we follow Bridgman's argument in full detail we appreciate the fundamental difference between his attempt to solve the paradox and the attempt of others, in spite of the fact that others also have based their answer on a discontinuity in the limiting process. Their solutions, however, are merely *ad hoc*.

Max Planck, for instance, after showing that the increase of entropy at the diffusion of two gases is given by $(-n_1 \ln c_1 - n_2 \ln c_2)$, where n_1, n_2 are the number of molecules, c_1, c_2 are the concentrations of the two gases respectively, he says:

> It also appears that the increase of entropy depends wholly on the number of the molecules n_1, n_2 and not on their nature, e.g. molecular weight of the diffusing gases. The increase of the entropy does not depend on whether the gases are chemically alike or not. By making the two gases the same there is evidently no increase of the entropy since no change of the state ensues. It follows that the chemical difference of two gases or in general two substances cannot be represented by a continuous variable. . . .[2]

Thus he states quite clearly that the discontinuity *follows* from the evident absence of increase of entropy and not the opposite way round as it is with Bridgman. For once we have adopted the methodological rule to check, by tracing the operations in terms of which concepts are defined, whether they are identical concepts or different ones, then without ever having been made aware of the lack of increase of entropy on self diffusion—thus without having been puzzled by any paradoxes at all—the difference in meaning that might exist between the process of diffusion when applied to

[1] P. W. Bridgman, *The Nature of Thermodynamics* (Cambridge, Mass., 1943), p. 169.
[2] M. Planck, *Treatise On Thermodynamics*, Dover Publications, p. 222.

different gases and when applied to elements of the same gas, would present itself to our mind.

For with a complete absence of convection currents how do we know at all that a continual intermingling of the elements of a gas takes place ? This follows from our kinetic picture of gases, according to which a gas, which is at complete rest macroscopically, consists of molecules rushing about at enormous speeds. Now nobody wants to say that the propositions of the kinetic theory of gases are meaningless. They are acknowledged as legitimate scientific propositions, since the indirect verifications to which they are amenable are regarded as adequate. But nevertheless, the process of intermixing that goes on between the elements of the same gas, the existence of which follows only from the kinetic picture, and the process of mixing that goes on between the parts of different gases —which of course follows also from the kinetic picture but in addition to this can also always be detected by the more direct instrumental operations through which different gases are identified— will appear essentially different processes, when we look at the matter from an operational or verificational point of view. Admittedly, we would be in no position to foretell the nature of the manifestation—if any—of such difference in the meaning of diffusion, but when presented with the paradox, all we have to do is to correlate the abrupt change in the behaviour of our system with regards to entropy increase, with the abrupt change in the meaning of the assertion that the process has taken place.

Planck's explanation, however, is an aposteriori one. Furthermore, his justification of the existence of such discontinuity, namely, that chemical constitution varies in whole numbers, does not satisfactorily explain the special significance of the discontinuity of the last step in the limiting process, because throughout the whole process of approaching similarity we are dealing with variations in terms of whole numbers.

The same methodological instrument for the comparison of law and concepts can be used to similar effects in mathematics. Admittedly the laws or theorems of mathematics are not verified but deduced or proven. But differences in the way related theorems are deduced or proven may lead to the detection of fundamental differences in the nature and function of such theorems. Similarly the concepts of mathematics are not defined in terms of instrumental operations but in terms of mathematical operations. But differences in these may also reveal basic differences in the concepts involved.

The following is a simple illustration from mathematics. Consider the concept of 'sum'. We know that only after the strange properties of the sum of an infinite series had kept the 17th- and 18th-century mathematicians baffled for a long time did they begin to realize that the 'sum' of an infinite series must be a different concept from the 'sum' of a finite series. The former is not really a 'sum' but, as it is usually put, it is a 'limiting value'.

Now the application of operational or verificational analysis could indicate this at once. The meaning of 'sum' depends on the operation of summing. In the case of a finite series, summing can always be performed by adding one term to the next, their sum to the next and so on. With an infinite series, however, the process of summing is never actual addition of the individual terms one to the other, but some different operation such as the elimination of all terms except the first and the last, integration or the like. Thus the difference in the operation of 'summing' might have served as an indication of the existence of basic differences in the nature of the two concepts.

Both examples, although so widely apart in content, one being taken from physics and the other from mathematics, illustrate the very same idea. In both cases we are dealing with related concepts. Diffusion of gases of different elements into one another, and self-diffusion, are related concepts because if self-diffusion is meaningful as deriving from the kinetic picture of gases, the diffusion of different gases is included just as much in that picture. The concept of the sum of finite series is also related to the concept of the sum of infinite series, since the devices by which infinite series are summed work with finite series as well. The fundamental difference, however, between the related concepts is in both cases revealed by the fact that one of the concepts can be defined operationally in an additional way, whereas the other concept cannot be so defined.

The differential function of operational or verificational analysis as brought forward by these examples should sharply be distinguished from another alleged function sometimes implied by a more extremist and rigid view. A number of expounders of operationism seem to ascribe a wider function to the differential principle, lending it an inflexible character but without increasing its usefulness. This conclusion is definitely not entailed by the view implied by the previous examples of the uses of differential analysis.

H. Dingle, for example, who is an enthusiastic supporter of operationism, insists that distances measured directly by laying measuring rods end to end and distances measured by triangulation method where we observe the angles subtended at the eye by the two extremities and then apply calculations, are not the same but two distinct quantities which, if we are to be consistent, ought to be called by two different names, such as, say, 'distance' and 'remoteness'. Or for example he explains that:

> ... the results yielded by our ten methods of finding surface tensions are not ten strivings after the same ideal but ten independent quantities which we have discovered to be approximately equal.[1]

This sort of attitude does not seem to serve a useful purpose. One feels in sympathy with R. B. Lindsay when he says:

> But such an isolation of concepts could defeat the very aim of physical science which is to provide a simple and economical description in terms of a minimum number of concepts.[2]

But Lindsay's criticism of the insistence upon splitting one concept into as many particulars as the number of ways it may be operationally defined does not affect that constructive methodological principle I was trying to describe before. At the most, Dingle's principle is related to ours in a very remote fashion. Both might be claimed to follow from the maxim 'different operation, different meaning', but otherwise they are fundamentally dissimilar.

First of all they are dissimilar because they refer to different situations. 'Distance' and 'remoteness' are not two related concepts one of which is susceptible to a certain set of operations to which the other is not. 'Distance' and 'remoteness' is ostensibly one single concept and the only reason to split it into two is because it is definable in two different ways. The same is true about Dingle's ten surface tensions. 'Diffusion' and 'self-diffusion' on the other hand, or for that matter the 'summing' of finite series and the 'summing' or infinite series are manifestly not identical concepts, and the

[1] H. Dingle, 'A Theory of Measurement', *British Journal for the Philosophy of Science*, 1950.

[2] *Philosophy of Science* (Vol. 4 1937), p. 458.

additional factor that they are not susceptible to the same operations serves as an indication of their fundamental difference, to the extent of being governed by different laws.

The second point is that one is a principle to insist upon something, the other is a principle to expect something. Our principle implies no dogmatic insistence on creating differences where they cannot be detected. As a methodological rule it is merely tentative. Differences between concepts and propositions exhibited by operational or verificational analysis should serve as a forewarning that additional differences between them are to be expected. Consequently we should be cautious not to take it complacently for granted that laws found applicable to one will remain applicable to the other. But if, after all, no further differences between them have come to light, there is no point in persisting to argue that the concepts or propositions must be of fundamentally different natures.

Lindsay's criticism seems justified when directed against the separation of what should be regarded as a single concept. 'Distance' and 'remoteness' should be regarded as one single concept. There is no possibility for instance of distinguishing between the 'distance' from here to the railway-station and the 'remoteness' of the railway-station from here, but by the self same fact that the former is measured by laying measuring rods end to end all along the way from here to the railway-station, the latter by triangulation method.

But the distance between here and the railway-station is manifestly different from the distance between here and the next galaxy. It is different already by the virtue of the different magnitude assigned to them by whatever method they both were measured. Now we also find that most of the operations in terms of which terrestrial distances may be defined are irrelevant to intergalactic distances (which can be defined in terms of certain instrumental operations via comparatively very numerous theories and hypotheses, in all of which the value of the velocity of light plays an essential role). This should be interpreted as meaning—according to our principle—that we are dealing here with fundamentally different concepts of distances. Special relativity bears out our expectations.

According to our principle if we have a body at 15 °C then to give its temperature is to evaluate one concept only, whether this is done by means of a mercury thermometer, Pt-wire thermometer, gas-thermometer, or any other thermometer. But a temperature of 15 °C obviously means something different from a temperature of 15,000°C. When we analyse the situation verificationally, we also find that for instance a statement 'the temperature in this room is 15 °C' can be given meaning in more than a dozen ways, none of which is relevant to the statement 'the temperature at the surface of Sirius is 15,000°C'. The latter could be verified on the assumptions of radiation laws through the use of a radiation thermometer only. Having found such a fundamental difference we are put on our guard and expect 15 °C and 15,000°C to be evaluations of fundamentally different concepts of temperature. Experience in this case, however, does not confirm the hypothesis that temperatures of different degrees differ from one another in a basic fashion. No practical advantage is obtained therefore from continuing to maintain the existence of such a basic difference.

The big difference between the two interpretations of the differential function of operational analysis should by now be completely clear. The summing of infinite series, we said, was an entirely different sort of activity from the summing of finite series. The recognition of this difference to the extent of even renaming the former as 'finding the limiting value of the sum' should have followed from operational analysis. This, however, has nothing to do with Dingle's type of analysis which resulted in the renaming of distance as 'remoteness'. That the summing of infinite series is not identical with the summing of finite series is obvious anyhow, as the object of summing is not the same in the two cases. In fact, the summing of 2 and 2, and the summing of 2 and 3, are not quite identical activities. But in the former case a fundamental difference is involved and this is indicated by the fact that the summing of infinite series can be affected only by entirely different kinds of operations from the summing of finite series.

In view of our discussion of Maxwell's criterion of physical reality in the last chapter, a criterion which is adopted by Bridgman as well, it will be of interest to note that Dingle's interpretation of the differential function of operational analysis is thought to have originated with Bridgman himself. Lindsay's criticism, for instance, was specifically directed against Bridgman. Another reviewer of Bridgman's philosophy, also assuming that the insistence upon the erection of as many categories of laws and concepts as the number of methods of verification and the number of methods of operational definition is an organic part of operationism, would even attribute to Bridgman the absurd consequence that 'there are as many Pythagorean theorems as techniques of demonstration'.[1]

But when we remember our discussion in the previous chapter, it will appear obvious to us that Bridgman would not subscribe to Dingle's views. For we have seen that the existence of two independent sets of operations in terms of which a concept may be defined is taken as an indication that the concept concerned stands for a 'real' property. That is, not only do we not subdivide such a concept but on the contrary we declare it to have an existence that goes, as it were, beyond these operations. Thus when we see that one can employ an Hg-thermometer in terms of which to define the temperature of a body and we can also employ a Pt-wire thermometer for the same purpose, we do not conclude that the two instruments are recording two different types of temperatures. What we conclude is rather that, unlike arbitrarily stipulated concepts which are not manifested in any other way but the way in which they were originally defined, temperature is not merely what the thermometer measures. It is a real property of bodies. The existence of temperature transcends any of the methods which define it. We no longer think of the set of readings on the Hg-thermometer as a definition of what temperature is, but as one of its manifestations. When we regard a concept as representing a real property we expect further manifestations of it, in addition to the two manifestations which have conferred the status of 'real' upon it.

5. THE GENERAL FUNCTION OF COMPARATIVE ANALYSIS

Operational or verificational analysis may serve as an instrument for comparing the ways in which concepts and propositions are related to one another in meaning and nature. In the foregoing section we have indicated the practical aspects of such comparison. We have seen how related concepts which would have been classified in the same category have been exposed as fundamentally different from another by this method of comparison. The comparative function of the analysis of meaning is, however, not confined to differentiation. The converse too can be affected. Concepts which on other grounds would have been regarded as funda-

[1] *British Journal for the Philosophy of Science*, Vol. 9, 1958, p. 76.

mentally different, as being associated with different laws, may have their kinship and likeness revealed through such analysis. The following will be an example of this. At the same time it will illustrate what we said in the introduction to this essay and tried to exhibit in every principle dealt with so far as a distinguishing feature of methodological principles, namely, that they guided the activities of scientists before they were articulated. They have been, so to speak, employed intuitively and have produced results prior to their explicit formulation.

This example concerns Oersted's work on electro-magnetic action. Oersted discovered, in 1821, that when a magnet capable of turning about a pivot is placed in the neighbourhood of a wire through which electric current is passing it will be acted upon by a force, as can be witnessed from the magnet's being set into motion. Next he started to wonder whether the counterpart of the same phenomenon would also take place, namely, whether a current carrying movable wire would experience a ponderomotive force when placed near a fixed magnet. The answer to this, of course, can easily be found by performing the simple experiment of placing a movable electric wire in the proximity of a magnet—an experiment eventually carried out by Oersted himself. However, before applying himself to the performance of this experiment Oersted predicted its result with complete certainty and said:

> As a body cannot put another in motion without being moved in turn when it possesses the requisite mobility it is easy to foresee that the galvanic arc must be moved by the magnet.[1]

I should like to draw special attention to the confidence with which Oersted asserted in advance the outcome of his experiment. On the surface, at least, it would seem highly questionable whether on the basis of the existing evidence he was justified in being so sure in making this pronouncement. And of course I do not mean merely questionable from the point of view of pure logic, but from the point of view of what may be regarded as the general practice in which scientific generalizations are made.

Oersted used in his argument two generalizations:

(i) His original result, namely, that a movable magnet is set into motion under the influence of an electric current.

---

[1] Quoted by E. T. Whittaker, *A History of the Theories of Aether and Electricity* (Thomas Nelson & Sons, 1951), p. 83.

(ii) Newton's third law of motion, e.g., that for every action there is an opposite reaction.

Now with regard to his second generalization, serious doubts could be raised. Is causing a magnet to rotate by an electric current an action? At any rate, is it the type of action to which Newton's third law is known to apply? The system with which Oersted was faced was after all fundamentally different from those for which Newton's third law had been tested. Newton was dealing only with actions of mechanical origin, when bodies impart to one another momentum through pressure, tension or through gravitational attraction. In all these cases the source of action was in the masses of the moving bodies. In Oersted's system on the other hand, the action was of electric and magnetic origin.

Besides the fact that the two types of forces come into being through totally different circumstances so that it should not have seemed reasonable to class them automatically into the same natural kind, one may also mention a positive reason why it could have appeared only too plausible that Newton's Third Law, while it applied to mechanical action, did not apply to electro-magnetic action. A mechanical system is symmetrical; all its components are alike. They all have masses and the 'quantity of matter' contained in them is the source of the forces that come into play. It is reasonable, therefore to suppose that all the components are equal partners in the interaction, they act and are acted upon to the same extent. Not so in Oersted's system where lack of reciprocation should seem natural. Here the two interacting components are different from one another. It would not seem unreasonable that the wire in which electric current was flowing was the 'active' and the magnetic bar of metal the 'passive' partner in the interaction.

Let us, however, ignore these aspects of mechanical and electro-magnetic action and let us concentrate on the question, how do we verify the proposition 'A force is acting here'? One possibility is to examine the bodies involved and if they are found to be of such kind that it is known that all bodies of this kind attract or repel one another in accordance with an established law of physics this should amount to a confirmation that a force is acting between them. But obviously the quickest and most direct method of verification is by observing the relevant masses acquiring accelerations. Now if we assume that when investigating whether certain phenomena do or do not belong to the same natural kind, the significant clues to look for are neither the origins of these phenomena, nor the circumstances or causes that have given rise to them, but that the clues are rather to be found in examining the resemblances and differences in the methods whereby statements about these phenomena are most immediately verified, then indeed mechanical and electro-magnetic actions are of the same natural kind. On this assumption Oersted's approach ceases altogether to seem surprising.

Oersted's reasoning, which ignored the above-mentioned differences between the interaction of masses and the interaction of electric currents and magnets, implies—unconsciously perhaps—the adoption of the methodological rule that when comparing concepts to one another we should compare the operations in terms of which they are defined. The significant features which determine whether certain phenomena ought to be classed in the same category or not are not the characteristics of the physical factors that were instrumental in bringing about these phenomena but their most direct operational manifestation.

If we follow closely the history of the concept of force from pre-Newtonian times till our days, we can observe a continual development in the same direction of concentrating more and more on the operational effect of force as its characterizing feature. This process started with the unification of celestial and terrestrial mechanics, which in spite of the seemingly vast differences in the nature of the moving bodies involved were recognized to belong to the same natural kind, based on the same laws of motion.

The peak of this trend was perhaps reached in 1894 with the publication of the *Principles of Mechanics* by Heinrich Hertz. In Hertz's dynamics the traditional generators of motion—force, mass as well as energy—were abandoned. His fundamental principle was that every free mechanical system will remain in a state of rest or will continue to move uniformly along a straightest path—where 'straightest path' is defined in a certain way which is of no special concern to us here. The significant point is that Hertz proposed to apply his principle to every possible system even though most of the systems encountered in practice are not 'free-systems'. Hertz overcomes this difficulty by his ingenious introduction of 'concealed' motion. The appeal to concealed motions and imagined mechanical entities could be regarded as satisfying only in a philosophical climate where emphasis is mainly laid on the question what is the immediate verification of an assertion that something is or is not the case. By the end of the 19th century this attitude has become so prevalent that no uneasiness was felt in treating a mechanical aggregate whose behaviour was the object of immediate investigation as a part of a larger fictitious system as long as the motions actually observed were exactly what they would have been had the concealed part existed.

Oersted's reasoning is one of the more outstanding episodes in this chain of developments dramatizing the role of the verification principle in the growth of the science of mechanics.

6. CONCLUSION

The principle of verification does not place a methodological precision instrument into the hands of the scientist. It is easy to see why not. For let it be granted that always whenever concepts possess a number of common features and differ in some other, the relevant features to compare in order to ascertain whether they do belong to the same natural kind or are basically dissimilar, are the operational definitions of their properties. This does not yet provide us with an ascertained method of comparison, as there are no clear rules how to compare different sets of operational definitions to one another.

Operational definitions may differ from one another first of all in the nature of the instrumental operations on which they are ultimately based, and secondly in the nature and amount of theories and hypotheses through which they are connected to these operations. To what degree may they differ in either respect and still be regarded as the same kind of operational definitions?

For example, different gases like oxygen, hydrogen or nitrogen are identified by different sets of operations. Consequently a statement about the diffusion of oxygen into nitrogen is verified differently from a statement referring to the diffusion of hydrogen into nitrogen. The two statements obviously have a different meaning. Yet we are not to regard them as basically different concepts. The laws of diffusion are identical for both processes. Self-diffusion, however, is so fundamentally different from inter-diffusion as to form a kind for itself.

Now admittedly the concept of self-diffusion is much further removed from the group of concepts to which the diffusion of various gases into one another belongs, than are the members of that group removed from each other. Each instance of inter-diffusion, being a macroscopic process, is far more directly defin-able in terms of instrumental operations than is the microscopic process of self-diffusion. Yet the question still remains, what are the explicit rules according to which one arrives at this conclusion? What, in general, are the precise rules for determining whether certain differences are fundamental or not?

A similar sort of problem, it will be remembered, has been raised in the previous chapter with regard to the question what is to be considered a single disposition. We had to conclude that no definite rules have been laid down by anyone. The answer here too is that no such rules are provided. And yet the verificational criterion, even if it is far from being an infallible guide, can be of great service. It provides the right orientation. It indicates the direction where the relevant clues for comparison will be found. It shows in what region the significant features are to be searched for. By eliminating large zones where differences and similarities are irrelevant and may therefore be disregarded it helps us to concentrate on those facets of experience that are determinative in the classification of phenomena into their natural kinds.

Most scientists would, for instance, agree that one should not blandly assume that physical laws concerning terrestrial matter tested under normal temperatures apply to the behaviour of matter in the interior of stars. The reason is that a fundamental difference is sensed between temperatures of millions of degrees centigrade and normal temperatures which are measurable by such widely differing means. No such distinction is felt to exist between temperatures of $-35\,°C$ and $-45\,°C$ although the former is measurable, and the latter is not, by a mercury-thermometer. What must be the amount of difference between temperatures T_1 and T_2 before we start hesitating to extrapolate laws tested for T_1 and assume that they apply to T_2? There are no definite rules laid down to enable us to answer this question. This is where the operational criterion lacks precision.

At the same time it should be noticed that it has never occurred to anyone to worry whether temperature laws may be extended to phenomena where the *origin* of the heat differs from the origin of the heat for which the law was tested. Without hesitation we assume that it is of no consequence whatsoever whether the temperature is due to heat absorbed through radiation or conduction, generated by mechanical friction or nuclear fission. The verificational criterion has so much become an organic part of our judgment that we automatically reject certain aspects of concepts as irrelevant to their classification. Thus in spite of its imprecision the verificational criterion is capable of excluding from considerations certain features which play no part in determining the relationship between concepts. Through our adoption of the criterion we expect the relevant clues for the classification of concepts to be found, not in their causes, origins, the nature of the processes with which they are associated, or in any 'unoperational' aspect, but in the way they are most directly definable in terms of instrumental operations.

In this last case it is perhaps more immediately evident than in any of the previous cases that no simple answer to the question of the ultimate logical basis of our principle can be given. As long as we have to retain the proviso that the adoption of the verification criterion is not certain to lead to success, but only likely to do so, and as long as the principle lacks definite meaning due to the vagueness of the term 'same set of operations' it is difficult to take a clear stand on the problem of the objective basis of the principle. What one could safely assert is that whenever, in the scientists appraisal, the operational definitions of concepts differ fundamentally from one another they expect them to belong to different natural kinds, otherwise they expect them to belong to the same natural kind. But to say that the foundation of the principle is nothing more than this, to explicate the principle solely in subjective terms would be an oversimplification. A methodological principle that has continually been applied for so long is bound to leave its mark on the structure of the system of science. This system, as a result, becomes amenable to further expansion by the same method.

But whereas the objective connection, in the context of present day science, between the 'real' meaning of concepts, i.e., the meaning which genuinely reflects the nature of concepts and their immediate operational aspects, may have become too subtle and complex to be accounted for in a simple fashion, it is quite a simple matter to see the subjective connection. It is obvious why when it comes to the *grasping* of the meaning of something the more direct operational elements play a more prominent role.

Suppose an entirely new chemical compound was discovered. Imagine that the discoverer of the compound described accurately the proportion of the various substances required to produce the new compound, the exact pressure and intensity of electric field to which these substances must be subjected and all the other precise details of the conditions and circumstances which are needed for manufacturing the new compound. Suppose he also gave a full account of all the chemical and physical phenomena which accompanied the process which yielded the new substance. It seems that all this would contribute very little to a subjective clarification of the nature of the substance with which one would feel pretty well 'unacquainted'. On the other hand, if, instead, the discoverer stated that the new compound was inflammable; that it was of a yellowish colour; that it was highly volatile; that it was of a given hardness, specific gravity and melting point, he would have done much more in creating a feeling that we have a notion of the substance he has discovered.

INDEX

animism in science, 51–53
Archimedes, 79 n.
area, calculations of, 50, 57
Aristotle, 71

Barker, F. S., 27 n.
Boyle's law, 40, 53
Bridgman, P. W., 22, 68, 92 ff., 116, 118–119, 123–124, 129–130

caloric fluid, 20, 121
caloric theory vs. kinetic theory of heat, 62–67
Campbell, N. R., 88 ff.
Carnap, R., 121
Comte, A., 111
Coulomb's torsion balance, 64–65

Darwin, C. G., 117
Descartes, R., 79 n, 104
determinism, 51
Dingle, H., 127–130
Duhem, P., 21–22, 67

Einstein, A., 117–118
electric field, 98–99
electro-magnetic action, 131–133
emergence, the doctrine of, 48
Euclidean geometry, 50
evolution, the theory of, 50–51

Feigl, H., 111
Fermat's principle of least time, 17
Fermi, E., 68
Feuer, L. S., 18 ff.

flat earth hypothesis, 38
Frank, P., 117

Galileo, on simplicity, 18
Gibb's paradox in thermodynamics, 122–123

Hafnium, the discovery of, 13, 16
Hertz, H., 133
Hippocrates of Chios, 57
Hooke, R., 104
Huygens, C., 79 n.
hydraulic press, 59–61

Isomers, 90–91
isotopes, 90

Joule, J. P., 62–66
Jupiter's satellites, 26

Kapp, R. O., 12 ff.
Kemeny, J. G., 27 n, 34
Keynes' postulate of limited variety, 2
kinetic theory, 51, 125
Kneale, W., 27 n., 28
Kuhn, T. S., 42

Lazerowitz, M., 113 n.
light rays, the structure of, 104–105
Lindsay, B., 127–129

Mach, E., 61 ff., 79 ff.
machines, natural and man made, 69–70

Margenau, H., 34
Maxwell, J. C., 95 ff.
Michelson-Morley experiment, 119

Nagel, E., 53
natural kinds, 2, 132–136
Neptune, the discovery of, 24–26, 31
Newton, his law of gravitation, 16; his mechanics, 22; his work on optics, 105; his third law of motion, 131–132
nuclear forces, 14, 16

Oersted, 131–134
Oppenheim, P., 46 ff.

Pascal, B., 59–61
perpetual motion, the impossibility of, 59, 61
Planck, M., 124–125
Planetary systems: Ptolemaic vs. Copernican, 32–33, 41–42; Copernican vs. Keplerian, 34–35

Poincare, H., 24, 52
Popper, K. R., 27 ff.
principle of least action, 51–52
Putnam, H., 46 ff.

Reichenbach, H., 111, 114–115
relativity, special theory of, 117–121
Russell, B., 10

Schlick, M., 113–114
Smart, J. J. C., 70 n.
stability of nuclea, 13–14
statistical mechanics, 22, 69
Stevin, S., 59
sum of mathematical series, 126

Taylor, B., 100
thermoelectrometer, 63
Turner, J., 97

vacuum, the impossibility of, 12–13, 15

Whittaker, E. T., 131 n.
Wittgenstein, L., 71